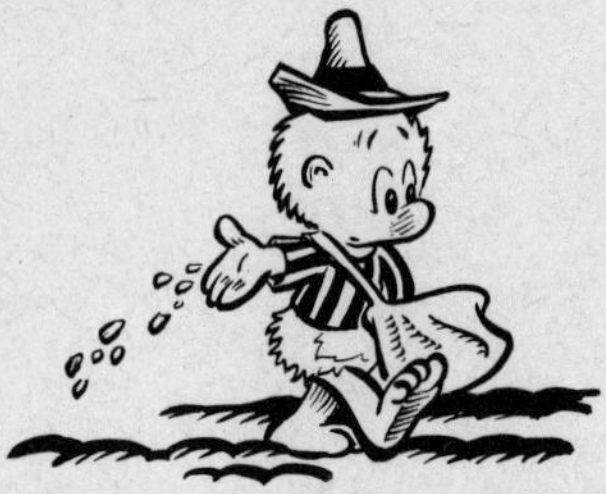

OTHER POGO BOOKS

POSITIVELY POGO

POGO'S SUNDAY PUNCH

THE POGO PARTY

THE POGO SUNDAY BOOK

POTLUCK POGO

POGO PEEK-A-BOOK

THE INCOMPLEAT POGO

THE POGO STEPMOTHER GOOSE

THE POGO PAPERS

UNCLE POGO SO-SO STORIES

I GO POGO

POGO

The POGO SUNDAY PARADE

BY WALT KELLY

SIMON AND SCHUSTER · NEW YORK

ALL RIGHTS RESERVED
INCLUDING THE RIGHT OF REPRODUCTION
IN WHOLE OR IN PART IN ANY FORM
© 1953, 1954, 1958 BY WALT KELLY
PUBLISHED BY SIMON AND SCHUSTER, INC.
ROCKEFELLER CENTER, 630 FIFTH AVENUE
NEW YORK 20, N. Y.
FIRST PRINTING

MANUFACTURED IN THE UNITED STATES OF AMERICA
PRINTED BY REEHL LITHO COMPANY, NEW YORK
BOUND BY SENDOR BINDERY, NEW YORK

Contents

BACK TO EARTH	9
VERSE	21
WOWF	23
ALL IN THE WASH	27
DOWN TO BEAR AND BRASSY FACTS	34
ROWL	38
TURTLE SLOOP	45
AHEAD IN THE POT	55
WORTH TUNA BUTCH	59
OCTOPOSSIBLE	69
FIGMENTALITY	76
A GOOD SPOT FOR A DOG	81
VERSE	90
A GREAT IDEA	92
A DILLARD, A DULLARD, A TEN-O'CLOCK SKULLER	95
A DEEP IN THE SLEEP	100
TWO THREE-MINUTE HEADS	108
REINDEER DON'T REIN IN VAIN, DEAR	112
THOOD FOR FOUGHT	116
ALL SWELL	124
A FEW BACKWORDS	126

Dedication

For Ruth, David, Kenny
And Ann and the many
Others plus Peter
And Tony (who's sweeter
than tooth paste) and Steven
And Andrew and even
The Oho, the Kit Kat
And that's about that....
Except, of course, Paul.....
Is that really all?

Back to Earth

"Hold it!"

"Isn't Comrade Furtive wonderful? Only this morning he invented the camera so's we can take a good-bye picture."

Our story opens on the dark side of the moon where a small group of scientists plan to return to Earth bringing with them the secrets of the Universe, the chart of the stars, the keys to the Heavens.

"By Nab! When I say hold it, I mean **hold it!**"

"How can I hold it when I gotta shiver?"

"It's *against* the constitution to shiver, comrade... shivering is for people who *are* **cold**, people who are **weak**, frightened, unhappy..."

"I can shiver for all **four** reasons."

Comrade Morose, I orders you to send Comrade Pogo to Siberia.
It can't be done Beloved Leader, until we gets down to earth.
Send him by parcel post; send him by air mail.
But up here we don't got no Siberia.
You mean our moon, our splendid new possession, got no place worse than this here?
Everything up here is worse.
Please send me to Siberia! Compared to here, Siberia is Miami Beach.
Just for that you can't go.
What's wrong, Tovarish?
I never get any breaks... They won't send me to Siberia.
Us miserable common people is gonna revolt unless you gives us our rights....we demands you sends Pogo to Siberia.
Our revolution is outlawed all other revolutions...you're pinched.

11

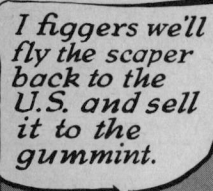

"I figgers we'll fly the scaper back to the U.S. and sell it to the gummint." / "**Good!** Then they kin rent it out to song writers an' everybody'll be rich."	"Exactly. A good snow moon ought to be worth a cool million." / "How you gonna get a hot moon into the country, though?"
"We'll **drop** it in... Say, right into Shibe Park... an' call it a ice meteor." / "Splendid."	"I sure gotta hand it to you, Comrade Boon Companion." / "We can sell tickets to our snow ball... We'll have two orchestras."
"What are those two little revolutionaries up to? Hmmph, they seem to be rolling a snow ball."	"Bah! Making a snow man. Playing children's games while we wears our brains out." / "Yes, just when we need every ounce of brain power at our command, two of our ounces is missing."

12

Panel 1:
- Well, a plague on **both** their houses, in case they makes igloos...Now what...?
- We gotta chart our course **back!**
- That's not it... no, no...
- What you lookin' for, Comrade Lugubrious?

Panel 2:
- As any fool would know, I'm lookin' for the square root of one so as to figure the angle of celebration on the disinclined pandemonium.
- We didn't **bring** no square roots.
- Didn't bring no **square roots?**
- Commander, you've plotted against the revolution.

Panel 3:
- You would destroy our sputnocks! You're a **skeptnic!** A **lunatnic!**
- Hold on! Hold on!
- Spitnik in his eyenik.
- What we brung is **round roots!** Square roots is outa date.
- **Round** roots?

14

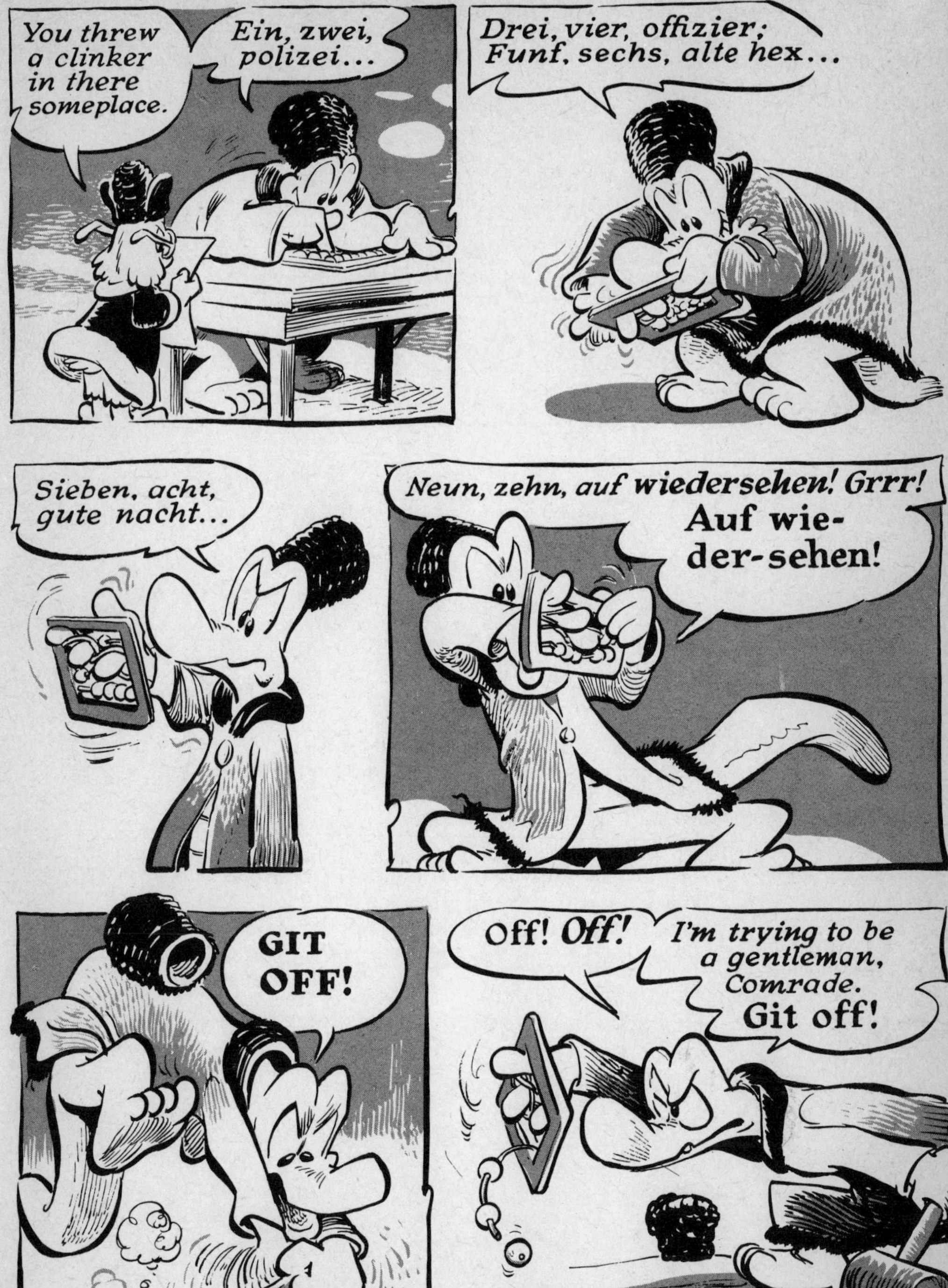

You threw a clinker in there someplace.
Ein, zwei, polizei...
Drei, vier, offizier; Funf, sechs, alte hex...
Sieben, acht, gute nacht...
Neun, zehn, auf wiedersehen! Grrr!
Auf wie-der-sehen!
GIT OFF!
Off! Off!
I'm trying to be a gentleman, Comrade. Git off!

16

17

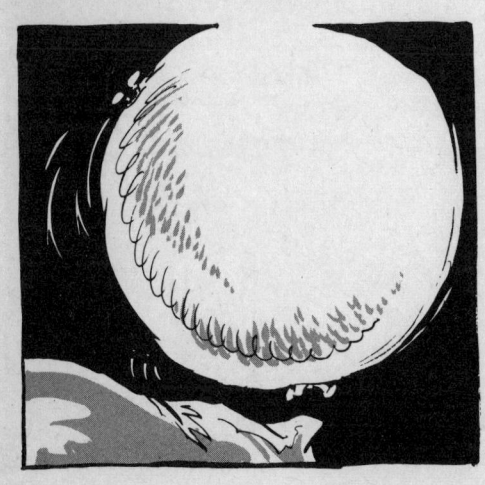

18

"I'm gonna end it all, comrades!"	*The discovery that the sun is made of strawberry ice cream sort of eases the heartbreak off his leave taking.*
"Yes, an' looka **this** nice big piece---just chuck full of nuts."	"Don't eat me! I'm a live orphan!" / "A snowman! A abominable snowman!"
"Two of 'em! They is abominable, all right; they is messin' up our ice cream." / "It's us, your Comrade Pals an' Friends."	**HISS!** / "That's a mighty loud an' portentious hiss."

Panel 1:

"Comrade Commander is blowin' up our rocket ship! He'll destroy the moon!"

"Yes! Yes! It's imbedded in solid ice cream—I'll shower the world with strawberry flavor."

"He's **mad, mad!** But why?"

"Because he didn't travel **Pan Am**."

Panel 2:

"Good-bye, Comrade Sidekicks, I---"

BAM!

Panel 3:

"You fell out of bed just in time to see the nice Independence Day fireworks, Albert."

"Oog! That ice cream!"

Panel 4:

"You ate practically a gallon of strawberry at the picnic--- but then, you're livin' in a country where a man's free---"

"---even to make a pig of himself if he wants."

"As a matter of fact, it's one of the things I got **against** it—why don't the gover'ment protect its citizens!?"

High G Over Whiz

Where the River wetful winds
The Spring doth spring
    and Fall
Becomes the Sum or total
    All
Of Winter's mournful minds.
Mind the children soon
    or late
And whistle in the dog;
There is no thaw, thin ice
    or fog
Nor thrift in fifty-eight.

A Roaming Candle

Rabbits are rounder
Than Bandicoots, Sam.
A Bunny's a Bounder
In old Alabam.

Thus is the Thistle
The thrush of the Thick,
And wet is the whistle
That winnows the wick.

ONE SUNDAY MORN AT BREAK OF BORN

Bacon and eggs
And pieces of pie,
Blue is my love
And red is her eye,
Purple her hair
As deep as the sky,
Hello there, Myrtle,
Hello and Goodbye.

WOWF
HOW CAN YOU LOOK SO INEPT AND UNKEMPT?
EASY!
IT'S ALL VERY WELL FOR YOU TO TALK--- YOU, WHO IS NEVER ADDRESSED A THRONG OF THOUSANDS OF SCREAMIN' CHILLUNS.
NEITHER IS YOU!
WHAT? I JUST DID!
THAT WAS MERE ME.
THAT WASN'T SO MERE-- YOU WAS SCREAMIN', WASN'T YOU?
QUIETLY, MAYBE QUIETLY.
AN' YOU'LL TELL THE STORY TO YOUR GRAN'CHILLUNS ETC. ETC. RUNNIN' INTO THOUSANDS--COUNT 'EM!
WAIT! SO FAR I ONLY GOT UP TO TEN-
DON'T CRITICIZE ME! I CAN OUT-THINK YOU; OUT-TALK YOU; OUT-OUT YOU AND ETC. ETC.
WHAT'S YOU MEAN: ETC?
I CAN OUT-ETC. YOU TOO.
YOU CAN NOT CAN NOT CAN NOT!
HONEST JOHN LARKIN

24

25

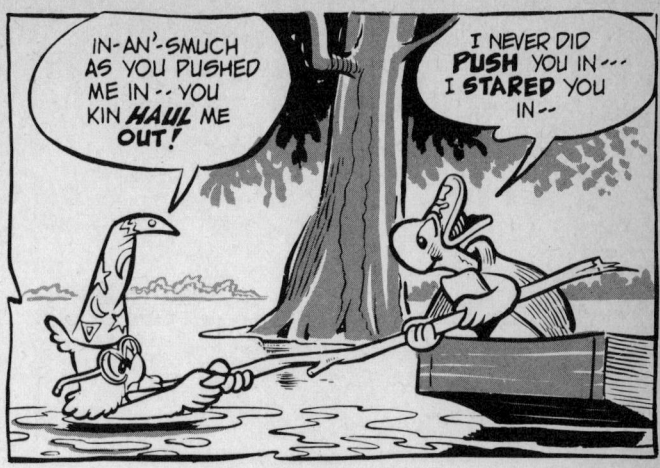

26

ALL IN THE WASH

"IT'S DAWN! DAWN!"

"Y'KNOW I DON'T GOTTA LAY AROUND LOOKIN' AT YOU --- I GOT OFFERS OF BETTER WORK!"

"YOU MEAN SOMEBODY IS OFFERED YOU A FEATURE PART IN A LAMB STEW?"

"NO -- I IS BEEN OFFERED THE MANAGERSHIP OF THE HEAVYWEIGHT CHAMPEENSHIP OF THE WORLD AN' OUTLYIN' TERRITORIES."

"EXCUSE A SMALL UNSTIFLEBLE NOTE OF DEERISION --- TO WIT: PHOO!"

"YOU MEAN TO TELL ME YOU IS GONE BE THE NEW MANAGER OF THE HEAVYWEIGHT CHAMP?"

"YEP."

28

YOU AIN'T GONE BE FIGHTIN' LADYBUGS-- UGH OOP.
YOU LEAVE HIM ALONE.
THE NERVE! HIM HITTIN' YO' LIKE THAT WHEN YOU WAS DOWN! HAVE A SAM'ITCH? I ALLUS PACKS A COUPLE INTO EVERY WET WASH.
GOODY! THANKEE! MY FAVORITE! LIVERWICH AN' HONEY.
?
MIZ BEAVER, YOU MAKES THE BEST HONEY AN' LIVERWURST SAM'ITCHES I EVER TASTED.
AN' THE ONLY---
ONLY? I THUNK YOU SAID THEY WAS YO' FAVORITES?
ANYTHING HANDY IS PERTY FAVORITE.
PARM ME, LADY, BUT THEY IS A STIFF IN YO' WASH.
HE GOT A NERVE!
SOME POOR STOWAWAY GOT STARCHED.

SEE THEM POOR PITIFUL FEET POOKIN' OUT FROM UNDER BENEATH OF YO' WASH? --- IT SHOW THAT SOME UNFORTUNATE CRITTUR IS PERISHED PERCHANCE, OR IS RENDERED HORS DE COMBAT.
NO -- TAIN'T NO HORSE, SON, AN' I IS PRACTICAL POSITIVE IT AIN'T NO WOMBAT!
LESSEE - WHERE WAS WE LAST WEEK --? UM - UH - THAT'S MY MANAGER!
THAT'S MY WASH BASKET AN' CONTINENTS, THAT'S WHAT!
WULL, THE PART WHAT'S MY MANAGER IS THIS HERE!
A FOOT.
THE BUG'S RIGHT -- HOW COULD A FOOT BE YOUR MANAGER?
NOT JES' ONE FOOT, BOTH FOOTS.
WHAT'S YOU NEED A TWO-FOOTED MANAGER FOR?
I NEEDS A TWO-FOOTED MANAGER SO WHEN HE PUTS HIS FOOTS DOWN IT'S GONNA BE DEFINITE -- LIKE THIS!
KEERFUL! SKOOSH A BUG AN' WE GITS RAIN!
CHOMP
CHOMP
CHOMP
SOMETHIN' IN THIS PILE OF WASH IS CHOMPIN' --
THAT'S MY MANAGER --

LOOKY THERE! YO' MANAGER GOT INTO MY SECRET CACHE OF SAM'ITCHES--AN' IS ET ALL OF 'EM.
OOG.
YOU SHOUNTNA KEP' 'EM IN THE WETWASH.
HOWDJA LIKE THE LIVERWURST AN' HONEY KIND?
WHEN I SAYS "OOG!" DOES THAT SUGGEST ANYTHIN'?
YOU DON'T GOTTA BE SO SMART--YOU ET PART OF THE WASH TOO--MR. GRIZZLE BEAR GOT TWO UNDERWEARS AND A SOCK MISSIN'!
YOU BETTER GIT MOVIN' BEFORE OL' BEAR MOVES YOU.
OOG I CAN'T MOVE.
POOR THING... HE'S SICK! WE'LL TOTE HIM IN THE BASKET.
HOT DOG! I LOVES BASKET RIDES.
HE AIN'T HALF AS SICK AS ME--JES' LOOKIN' AT HIM RIDIN' MAKES ME SICK.
JES' LOOKIN' AT YOU DOIN' ANYTHIN' AIN'T EXACTLY A CURE-ALL.

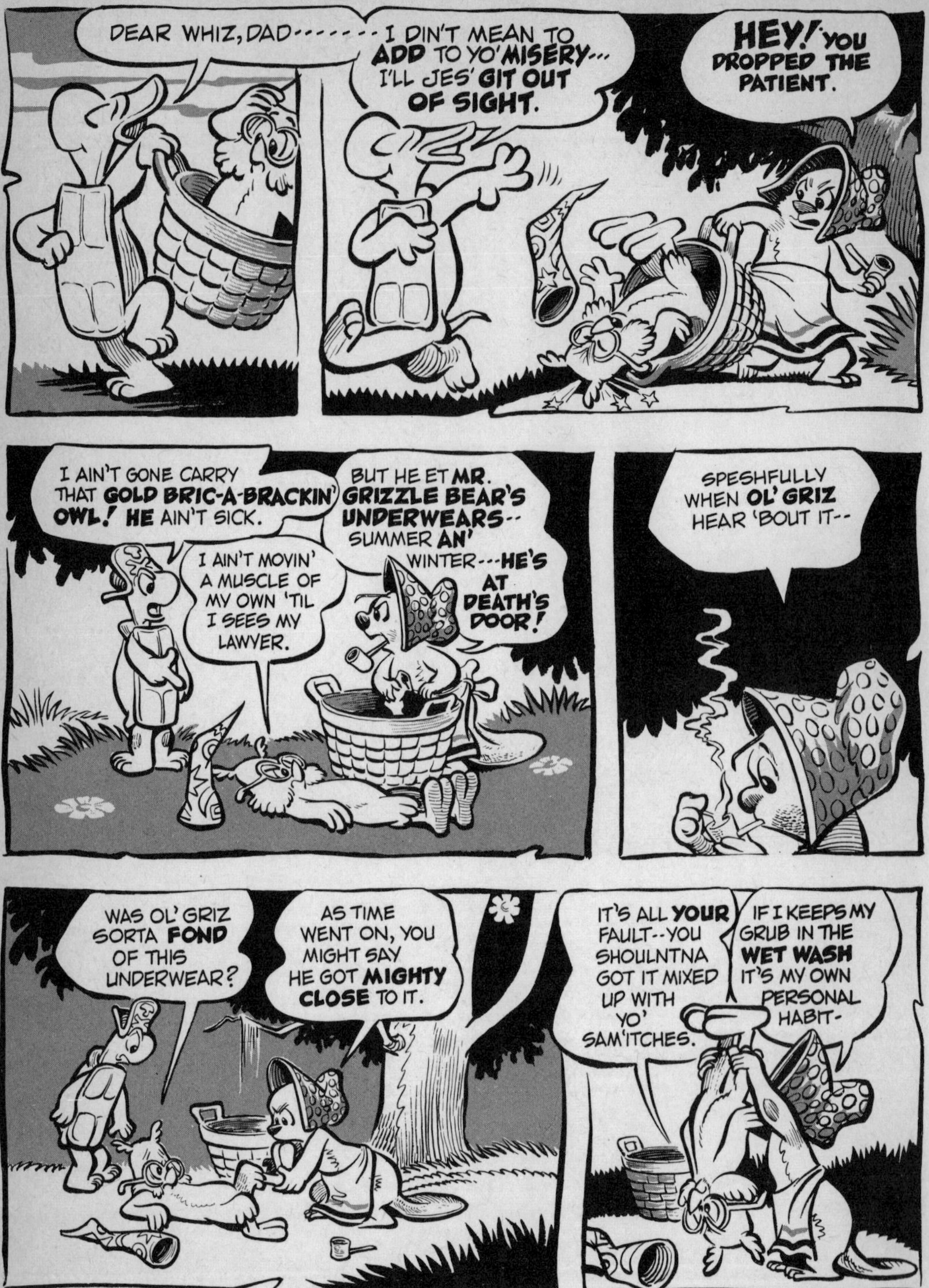
DEAR WHIZ, DAD-------I DIN'T MEAN TO ADD TO YO' MISERY... I'LL JES' GIT OUT OF SIGHT.
HEY! YOU DROPPED THE PATIENT.
I AIN'T GONE CARRY THAT GOLD BRIC-A-BRACKIN' OWL! HE AIN'T SICK.
I AIN'T MOVIN' A MUSCLE OF MY OWN 'TIL I SEES MY LAWYER.
BUT HE ET MR. GRIZZLE BEAR'S UNDERWEARS-- SUMMER AN' WINTER---HE'S AT DEATH'S DOOR!
SPESHFULLY WHEN OL' GRIZ HEAR 'BOUT IT--
WAS OL' GRIZ SORTA FOND OF THIS UNDERWEAR?
AS TIME WENT ON, YOU MIGHT SAY HE GOT MIGHTY CLOSE TO IT.
IT'S ALL YOUR FAULT--YOU SHOULNTNA GOT IT MIXED UP WITH YO' SAM'ITCHES.
IF I KEEPS MY GRUB IN THE WET WASH IT'S MY OWN PERSONAL HABIT-

AN' I AIN'T GONE HAVE MR. GRIZZLE BEAR BLAMIN' **ME** FOR THE DEMISE OF HIS SMALL CLOTHES -- YOU GOIN' OVER HIS PLACE AS EGG-ZIBBIT NUMBER "A".
MAM AN' ME IS HEAR UNCLE OWL GOT A CASE OF THE **DREADFULS**.
MY! HE **DO** LOOK BAD---NOT LIKE HISSELF AT ALL -- MAM SENT SOME **SCALDY TEA** -- **SASSAFRASH IT IS**.
SHE SAY **DRINK IT ALL** AT ONCE **HOT** OFF'N THE FIRE AN' IT'LL CURE **OR** WORSEN ANYTHIN'.
HOOP!
WAWP!
CALL THAT **SICK?**
MAM'S SASSAFRASH TEA REALLY BRISK UP A BODY---HE LOOK LIKE HISSELF NOW.
THEM WONDER DRUGS BEAT ALL.
WHILE YOU IS UP PICK UP MISTER BEAR'S WASH WHAT YOU STREWED ABOUT.
YOOP
YOOP
YOOP
YOOP

DOWN TO BEAR AND BRASSY FACTS

HERE'S THE REST OF MR. GRIZZLE BEAR'S LAUNDRY---- IF IT AIN'T **ALL** HERE, MEBBE HE CAN'T COUNT **NOHOW**.

OH, HE CAN COUNT GOOD ENOUGH-- AN' HE GONNA COUNT ON GIVIN' YOU **WHATFOR** WHEN HE SEE YOU IS ET HIS **SOCKS** AND **UNDERWEARS**.

PEEK!

THERE'S **ANOTHER** THING--- YOU ET A CHONK OUTEN HIS **CAMISOLE**---- ALL NEXT WINTER HE GONNA HAVE A **FRIGID BELLY BUCKLE**--- AN' NOTHIN' MAKE A GRIZZLE BEAR **MADDER** NOR A **COLD TUM BUTTON**.

ALL **I** GOT TO SAY, OWL, IS THAT OL' GRIZZLE BEAR IS GONE **SCOLD** YOU 'TIL YOU IS **BLACK AN' BLUE** ON **ACCOUNT** YOU ET HIS WASH.

THIS STRIKES **ME** AS BEIN' **YOUR** BIG OPPORTUNITY TO BE A REAL FIGHTIN' CHAMPEEN.

IT STRIKES ME AS BEIN' **YOUR BIG OPPORTUNITY** TO TRAVEL.

AH, YOUR LIGHTNIN' WIT INDICATES YOU IS GONNA BE ANOTHER CHAMP LIKE DOUGH PADUCAH! I CAN'T LEAVE NOW-- THIS IS MY BUSY SEASON.
YOU GONE GIT READY FOR THE FIGHT?
YOU IS GONE GIT READY FOR THE FIGHT!
ME?
KEERECT! I IS GONE TEACH YOU TO MESS 'ROUND WITH UPPERCUTS, CROSSCUTS, UNDERCUTS, LEFT JABS, PUN JABS AN' U-TURNS.
I AIN'T GONE DO IT.
WHY!?
I AIN'T GONE GIT MAD AT NOBODY.
AS YOU MANAGER, I ASKS YOU: WHAT'S YOU GONE DO IF I WAS OL' BEAR AN' COME SHOVIN' 'ROUND LIKE THIS?
SPLOP!
I GONE DO THIS!
YOU DOUBLE-CROST ME! YOU SAY YOU AIN'T GONE GIT MAD AT NOBODY.
THAT'S WHAT I'D DO IF YOU WAS OL' BEAR ... BUT LONG AS OL' BEAR IS OL' BEAR - HERE'S WHAT I'D DO.

ARRGH
WHAT?
WHY'S ANYBODY WANNA GO SAYIN': AARGH?
HEY, COME BACK!
WHY? I IS GOIN' YO' WAY ARREADY.
BUT I ONLY IS GOIN' AS FAR AS YOU--- SO HALT--HALT!
I WAS RIGHT BACK THERE JEST NOW--IF YOU WANTED ME SO MUCH WHY WASN'T YOU AROUND?
AAARGH
WISH I COULD REMEMBER WHY YOU IS CHASIN' ME--
DON'T WORRY! SOON'S I CATCHES YOU, I GONE REMIND YOU.

MEBBE YOU WANTS TO TELL ME YOU ADMIRES MY PERTY BROWN EYES.
NO FAIR! YOU IS PULLIN' A FOUL BY JUMPIN' OVERBOARD-- THE TURF CLUB SAYS NO RUNNIN' UNDERWATER.
'COURSE IF YOU COULD GIMME A GOOD SOLID REASON FOR COMIN' BACK, I'D THINK IT OVER.
I'LL BAKE YOU A BIRTHDAY CAKE, WHEN, AS AN' IF YOU HAS ONE.
THAT'S NOT A GOOD ENOUGH REASON-- ----UH-OOP!
WHOOSH! RIGHT ACROSS THE WATER WITHOUT TOUCHIN'- --DID YOU FIND A REASON FOR COMIN' BACK?
I SURE DID--- LOOKY THERE.
WHICH ONE OF YOU VARMINTS ET MY UNDER SHIRT?
OL' GRIZZLE BEAR.

ROWL
MAKE OUT LIKE WE IS **INNOCENT**.
YOU AND YOUR TASTE FER **LINGERIE**.
STOP RUNNIN'-- STOP RUNNIN'!
YOU LI'L' **VARMINTS!**
I'M **NOT** RUNNIN', --I WISHT I **WAS!**
WHICH ONE OF YOU **LI'L' RASCALS** ET MY **UNDER-CLO'ES**?
WULL; AS YOU KIN PLAINLY SEE, US IS A COUPLE OF ***LOVABOBBLE*** AN' **INNOCENT-TYPE** OF **MODEST YOUTHS**.
YES INDEED!
GROWGHF!

DON'T GO GIVIN' ME A LOT OF CITY TALK -- WHO ET MY UNDER-CLO'ES?
I CANNOT TELL A LIE --- EVEN THO' IT MIGHT RESULT IN DEATH!
DEATH ?
DEATH!
RIGHT!
YOU, YOU COWARD! YOU NO-GOOD, YALLER-TOED, LOW-BINDIN', LILY-LIVERED DOG! WHY COULDN'T YOU BE A MAN LIKE THIS OTHER FELLA?
WELL.
WHY NOT, PRAY TELL?
SPEAK UP!
WELL I -- WELL -- WELL - I - UH --- I
IT'S LOW LIFES LIKE YOU WHAT CAN'T CONFESS TO NOTHIN', AS MAKES MY HONEST BLOOD BOIL!

40

I'SE GONE SET HERE 'TIL YOU MAKES UP YO' MIZZERBOBBLE MIND TO COME OUT AN' CON-FESS YOU ET MY SMALL CLO'ES.
WULL, I GOT A PREE-POSAL.
THE WAY TO DECIDE WHO ET 'EM IS TO PER-FORM A AUTOPSY.
A AUTOPSY?
A AUTOPSY!
RIGHT! A AUTOPSY!
A AUTOPSY!? ON WHOM?
LESSEE, HOW MANY OF US IS THERE?
ON WHOM INDEED?
ON YOUM! THAT'S WHOM!

Panel 1:
WAIT A JES'A **DOGBONE** MINUTE--- DOES YOU MEAN **ME** WHOM OR **HIM** WHOM---? **WHO** WHOM?

YEAH!

OWL WHOM! THAT'S THE WHO WHOM WHOM IS WHO---!

Panel 2:
ON ACCOUNT OF **HOWLAND WHO OWL** IS THE CRITTUR WHAT ET THE HOLE IN YO' CAMISOLE AN' **DEE**-VOURED YO' PANTY-WAIST! **J'ACCUSE!**

Panel 3:
DON'T YOU CALL **ME** NO **JACCUSE!**

NOW TAKE IT EASY, FRIEND--- HE IS FEARLESS **CON**-FESSIN' YO' GUILT--- GIVE HIM CREDICK!

J'ACCUSE! J'ACCUSE! J'ACCUSE!

Panel 4:
I IS JES' HAD A QUIETLY BEAUTIFUL THOUGHT--- 'LONG AS THEM CLO'ES IS **YOURN**, MR. GRIZZLE BEAR, WHY NOT MAKE A AUTOPSY ON **YOU**?

IT'S ONLY FAIR--- THE AMERICAN WAY IS BEST.

Panel 5:
THE LITTLE **WHIPPERSNACKER** THERE GOT A VERY SOUND **LEGAL** POINT.

WHIPPER-WHAT?

HAW!

IS YOU DISPUTIN' MY FRIEND'S LEGAL POINT? WHAT'S YOU SAYIN' "HAW" AT?
AT YOU IS WHAT I'M SAYIN' IT AT----
PHOO!
STEP OUT HERE AN' SAY THAT, FRIEND.
FRIEND BEAR, TURTLE IS RIGHT --- IF YOU WAS THE OWNER OF THE CONSUMED SMALL CLO'ES -- THEN --
DON'T BOTHER ME, I IS WAITIN' FOR TURTLE TO STEP OUT LIKE A MAN.
BUT I INSIST -- IF THAT'S THE CASE, OUR TROUBLES ARE OVER!
HIS TROUBLES AIN'T OVER --- HE INSULTED ME AN' I GONE HANG 'ROUND OUTSIDE FER HIM.
YESSIR --- OUR TROUBLES ARE OVER -- WE'LL MAKE MILLIONS AN' LIVE LIKE KINGS.
HUH?
LIKE QUEENS, EVEN.

GOTCHA!
DID YOU REALLY GIT HIM?
YUP--- LEASTWISE IT 'PEARS I DO--- RIGHT IN MY HAN'S!
HEY.. WHERE'S MY HEAD?
HELP! HELP!
HEY! HE'S FLYIN' BLIND! HE'LL RUN INTO SOMETHIN'!
RUNNIN' WITHOUT A HEAD HE'LL SLAM INTO A TREE AN' KNOCK HIS BRAINS OUT.
OOP!?
WHAT BRAINS? HE AIN'T GOT NONE! ---LOOKY!
MY WORD! NOT EVEN ONE!

TURTLE SLOOP

HELP! HELP!

STOP!

THERE'S ONE NOW, LORENZO. ASK HIM!

IF YOU'RE A HEADLESS HORSEMAN, WHERE'S YOUR HORSE?

YOWP!!

MY WHAT?

DESTROY A SON'S FAITH IN HIS FATHER, WILL YOU?!

MY SAKES! JES' CAUSE I WAS RUNNIN' WITH MY HEAD TUCKED INSIDE MY SHELL, THEM LI'L' BUGS THOUGHT I WAS A *HEADLESS HORSEMAN.*

HEY, OL' TURTLE--- IT'S 'BOUT LUNCH TIME--- HOW 'BOUT EATIN' WITH ME?

BIRMINGHAM ALA   UNCLE CHARLIE FELL

GUESS I MOUGHT'S WELL--- THANKIN' YOU KINDLY.
HELP YO'SELF TO A OAR THERE.
UNCLE CHARLIE FELL
BIRMI
HAM
BY JING, I JES' GOT ABOARD--- WHY'S I GOTTA DO THE ROWIN'?
I ROWED UP TO HERE--- DIN'T I ?
MY MA DIN'T BRING ME UP TO ACK LIKE THAT --- SHE SAY NEVER IMPOSE ON OTHERS SMALLER AN' GENTLER NOR YOU.
MY PA WAS THE SAME--- HE SAY NEVER DEE-PRIVE OTHERS OF THE LI'L' PLEASURES AN' COMFORTS--- SO I LETS YOU ROW--
UNCLE CHARLIE
THE BIRMINGHAM NEWS
BESIDES I IS PLANNIN' THE MENU--- FOR WHEN US GITS TO YOUR PLACE FOR LUNCH--
MY PLACE!?
BIRMI
YOU IS A IRRESPOSSIBLE NO-GOOD! INVITES ME TO LUNCH IN MY OWN HOUSE --- SIMPLE COURTESY DEMANDS YOU DON'T GO INTO A MAN'S HOUSE 'TIL HE INVITE YOU!
INGRATE--INGRATE INGRATE--
BIRMIN
THUNK YOU'D BE FLATTERED--- UH, WHERE'S YOU GOIN' NOW ?
OVER TO POGO'S HOUSE--- HE ALLUS GOT APLENTY-- I ET ALL MY LUNCH FER BREAKFAST ANYWAYS.
OL' UNCLE CHARLIE

EITHER STOP DRAGGIN' YO' TAIL OR WIGGLE IT A LI'L'.
WHUFFO WIGGLE IT?
SO'S IT'LL ACK LIKE UNTO A **OUTBOARD MOTOR**.
MY SAKES! I NEVER **THOUGHT** OF THAT!
KEEP GOIN'! A DEE-LICIOUS AROMA WAFTS FROM YON POGO SHORE.
WHEE!
WHEE-HAWKEN!
MMM -- SEEM LIKE THIS **PER-LOO** NEED A LI'L' TOUCH OF SOMETHIN' ELSE.
JELLY BEANS AND OTHER CONDIMENTS

FULL SPEED AHEAD.
LESEE, THAT PERLOO NEEDS SOMETHIN'. SALT-- PEPPER-- MOLASSES? --- NO. UM --BUTTER SCOTCH? PEANER BUTTER--?!
P
OOF!
BUMP!
LAND A-
-HOY!
MM-- SNOW! SO EARLY IN THE SEASON!
WHAT HAPPENED TO OL' TURTLE?
TURTLE--? I DUNNO-- DIN'T SEE HIM. BUT YOU IS JES' IN TIME TO TASTE THE PER-LOO.
MM--SEEM LIKE IT DON'T TASTE GOOD AS USUAL.
THAT'S A INSULT!

POGO, YOU IS A BOUNDLESS BOUNDER! YOU ASK ME WHAT I THINKS OF THE PER-LOO AN' WHEN I TELLS YOU, YOU CLAIMS YOU IS INSULTED.
WHAT?
RIGHT! AN' BESIDES YOU IS A OVER-GROWED LIZARD!
THE SUPREME INSULT!
HOW KIN YOU INSULT A OLD AN' BOOZIM PAL LIKE ME IN SUCH A UNCOUTH MANNER?
I NEVER DID---THE PER-LOO SAID YOU WAS A LIZARD.
JELLY BEAN AN' ASSORTED SAUCES
LIES! DECEIT! NOTHING BUT FRAUDULENCIES!
TO THINK THAT A OL' CHUMSHIP SHOULD GO THIS WAY---POGO SAYIN' THAT THE PERLOO KIN TALK!
ANYBODY BUT A WALLEYED FROG LIKE YOU WOULD KNOW IT KIN!
THAT'S THE LAST NEEDLE THRU WHICH THE CAMPBELLS BROKE THEIR BACKS!

50

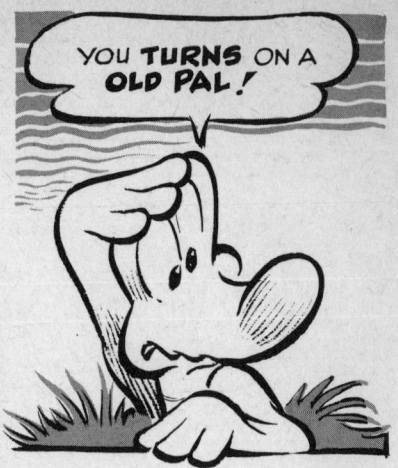

HERE I IS TASTIN' MY TONGUE TO THE BONE AN' YOU IS DOIN' NUTHIN' BUT THINKIN'
HOW IS THE PERLOO?
SINCE TURTLE WAS IN IT, IT GOT A PECULI-HORRIBLE FLAVOR-UGH!
NO WONDER! YOU JES' ET YO' SEE-GAR WITH IT····
WHOOSH! I IS GLAD YOU POINTED THAT OUT··· FOR A MINUTE I THUNK CHURCHY HAD SEE-GAR BLOOD IN HIM.
BY JING, I IS GONE FIND CHURCHY LA FEMME AN' ASK HIM WHY HE WAS HIDIN' IN MY PER-LOO.
BETTER TAKE ALONG THE EVIDENCE.
ON ACCOUNT OF IT IS SUCH A DEE-LICIOUS COMPANION.

52

WHAT YOU HIDIN' FOR? AIN'T NOTHIN' TO BE SKEERT OF.
OH NO? --- LOOKY THERE!
GOOMF! GOOMF! ROWR BAZZLE!
OH! WOE IS ME! HERE WE IS BEIN' CHASED BY A BIG HORNED MONSTER AN' ALBERT AIN'T NOWHERE IN SIGHT TO SAVE US.
THAT'S WHAT YOU GIT FOR TRUSTIN' A BIG BLOW HARD LIKE ALBERT --- HE'S NEVER AROUND WHEN YOU WANT HIM.
HERE! DUCK AHIND OF HERE AN' MEBBE THE MONSTER WON'T FIND US!
GOOMF! ROWR-BAZZLE!
GOOD! HE PASSED US BY--- WE IS SAFE!

Panel 1: FOR A MINUTE I THUNK HE WAS GONE COTCH US AN' EAT US AN' *ME* WITH NO CEMETERY PLOT.

Panel 2: UNCLE SASSAFRASH ALLUS SAID A BOY OUGHT TO BUY HISSELF A BURYIN' PLOT WITH HIS FIRST DOLLAR.

BUT, IF THAT MONSTER ET YOU AN' ME, WE WOULDN'T OF NEEDED NO CEMETERY PLOT --- WE'D OF BEEN OUT A DOLLAR EACH.

Panel 3: HOWEVER, IF THE MONSTER HAD A BURYIN' PLOT, US WOULD OF ALL BEEN INTERRED TOGETHER SOONER OR LATER --- MORE OR LESS --- AN' US WOULD OF SAVED TWO BUCKS.

AW -- THERE'S NO FUTURE IN SUCH INVESTMINTS.

Panel 4: I GUESS YOU'RE RIGHT -- IT'S A INVESTMINT FROM WHAT YOU WOULDN'T WANT *NO* RETURNS -- THERE IS NO FUTURE IN BEIN' DEAD.

Panel 5: Y'KNOW IF UNCLE SASSAFRASH KNEW THAT HE'D TURN IN HIS GRAVE.

THE QUESTION IS -- *WHAT WOULD HE TURN IT IN FOR?*

AHEAD IN THE POT
BY JING! THERE'S OL' UNCLE ALBERT.
UNCLE ALBERT, YOU IS LOOKIN' MOUGHTY GOOD THESE DAYS!
DAG NAG! CAN'T YOU SEE I GOT A POT STUCK ON MY HEAD?
YOU GOT A NICE COLOR.
'AT'S FUNNY--- I NEVER NOTICED---
I MERE THUNK YOU HAD GONE GOT YO'SELF A HAIRCUT.
UMF.
SO YOU GOT A POT STUCK ON YO' BEAN, UNCLE ALBERT? I THUNK YOU LOOKED A LI'L' CLEAN SHAVED.
YOU MUST GIT LONESOME, BEIN' IN THERE IN SOLITARY CONFINEMINTS!
GROWF!

HOW COME YOU GOT THAT MACHINE LOBBED OVER YO' DOME IN THE FIRST PLACE?
A CASE OF SHEER SKILL.
I WAS TASTIN' AT SOME DEE-LICORICE GOOP IN IT WHAT POGO COOKED. IN MY ENTHUSIASM, I LIFTS UP THE POT AN' ET MY WAY INSIDE, AS CLEVER AS COULD BE.
THING WHAT BOTHERS ME MOST IS: WHAT TIME IS IT?
CAN'T YOU TELL IF IT'S LUNCH TIME?
IT'S ALWAYS LUNCH TIME FOR UNCLE.
WHAT TIME YOU SAY?
WHEN YOU HEARS THE MUSICAL NOTE IT WILL BE EXACTLY...
BONG!
ONE O'CLOCK!
AAARGH!
WHY IS IT WHEN YOU DOES UNCLE ALBERT A FAVOR, HE ALWAYS GIT MAD?

POOR UNCLE ALBERT!
STUCK IN THAT POT!
AARGH!
IF YOU IS SO SORRY FO' HIM WHY'N'T YOU HELP HIM OUT OF IT?
OH, THAT WOULD NEVER DO!
NOT WHILE HE'S BUSY.
PHOO! WHAT'S HE SO BUSY AT?
AS YOU KIN PLAINLY SEE, HE'S BUSY CHASIN' US!
POOR UNCLE ALBERT! RUNNIN' WITH THAT HOT POT ON HIS HEAD.
SEEM LIKE THE LEAST YOU COULD DO IS HELP HIM OUT OF IT SO'S HE COULD SEE TO CHASE YOU BETTER.
WOULDN'T THAT BE A BREACH OF THE RULES?
YEAH, EVER'THING GOTTA BE FAIR AN' SQUARE, YOU KNOW.

SEE!? HE BANGED INTO A TREE!
IT WASN'T THE TREE'S FAULT--- IT WAS STANDIN' THERE MINDIN' ITS OWN BUSINESS.
WHAT'S THE BIG IDEE? KNOCKIN' ME DOWN!? YOU BLACKGUARD!
THAT POOR TREE.
WHY, YOU POT HEAD! WHO'S YOU TO CALL THE KETTLE BLACK? YOU BALL HEADED BULL BAT!
SAY THAT AGAIN!
RAT TAT TAT TAT
DING DING DING DING DING
HELLO?--- HELLO?-- WHAT A TIME FOR THE PHONE TO RING --- (ME IN THE MIDDLE OF A HEROIC DEED) HELLO?
SAVED BY THE BELL.

WORTH TUNA BUTCH

WHAT WAS YOU AN' THAT TURTLE TALKIN' ABOUT AFORE HE SO RUDIMENTLY RUN OFF?

AHA!

IT SO HAPPEN, FRIEND BEAR, THAT WE WAS TALKIN' 'BOUT *MILLIONS* OF DOLLARS!

LET ME *CORNGRANULATE* YOU --- THAT'S ONE OF MY FAVORITE SUBJECKS!

BULL--Y FOR YOU

OWL -- I ALWAYS WANTED TO TELL YOU WHAT A *FINE MAN* I THINKS YOU IS!

FEEL *FREE*, FRIEND BEAR.

I *LIKES* THE THINGS YOU TALKS ABOUT --- 'SPECIALLY WHEN YOU TALKS 'BOUT *RICHES*.

I *DO* HANDLE IT WELL.

AN' I THINKS IT WAS *MIGHTY CUTE* OF YOU -- TO BE TALKIN' WITH TURTLE (LIKE YOU SAY,) ALL 'BOUT *MILLIONS* OF DOLLARS.

AW.

HOW MANY MILLIONS?
HOW MANY MILLIONS OF WHAT?
DOLLARS-- OUR HONORABLE SUBJECK WAS.
OH-- ME AN' TURTLE WAS TALKIN' 'BOUT COUNTLESS MILLIONS.
BY NAB! STEP INSIDE HERE AN' OL' MIZ BEAR WILL FOTCH YOU A VITTLE.
THANKEE KINDLY.
I UNNERSTAND YOU IS TALKIN' 'BOUT 'NOUGH MILLIONS FOR US ALL! RIGHT?
RIGHT!
IF I KNEW ANYBODY WAS GIVIN' AWAY MILLIONS, I'D ASK FER SOME FER YOU TOO---- THAT'S WHAT TURTLE AN' ME WAS TALKIN' 'BOUT--- SHARE AN' SHARE ALIKE.
HOW'S YO' FRIEND LIKE THE PERLOO?
HE LOST HIS HEAD OVER IT.

61

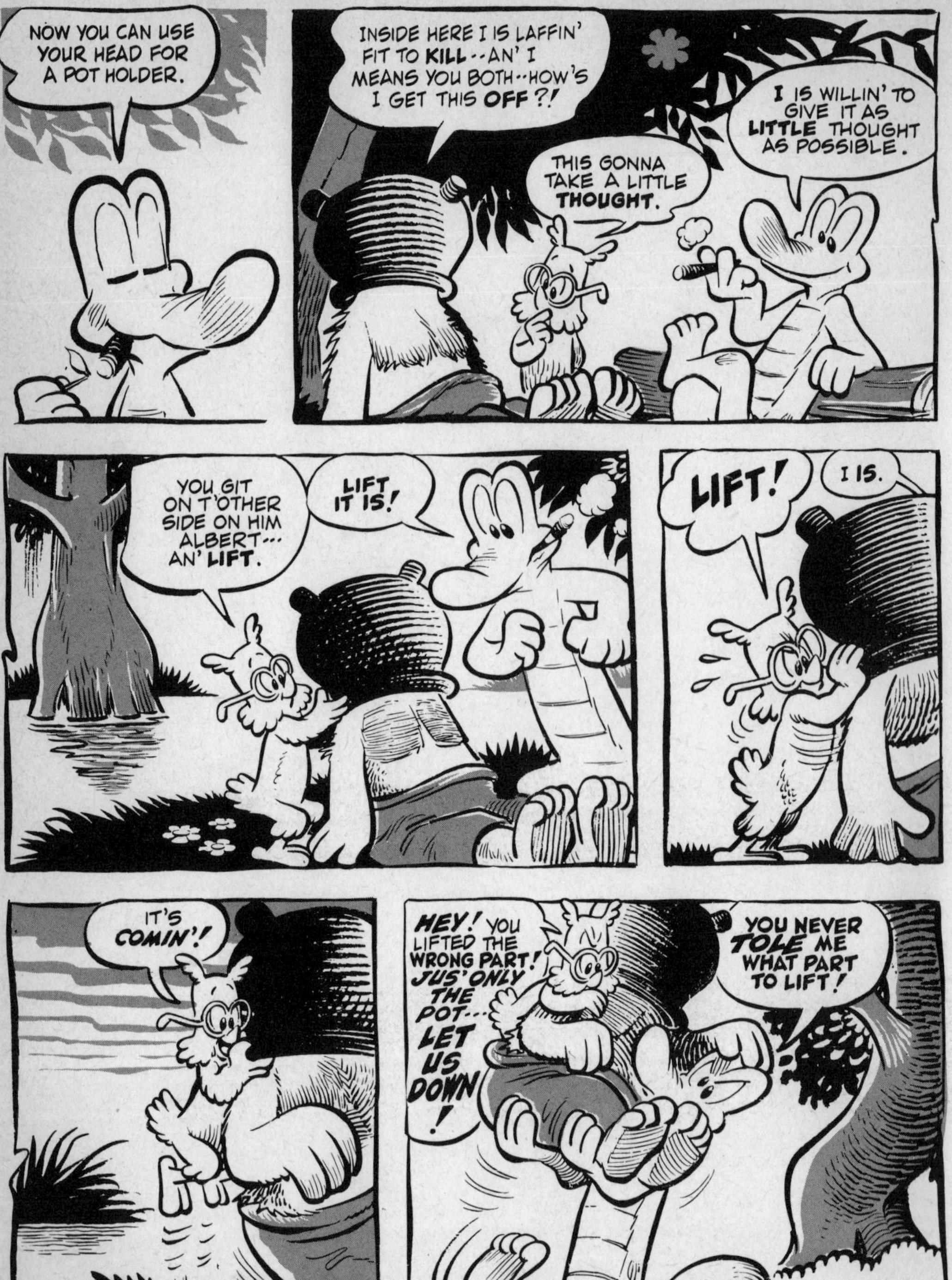

NOW YOU CAN USE YOUR HEAD FOR A POT HOLDER.
INSIDE HERE I IS LAFFIN' FIT TO KILL--AN' I MEANS YOU BOTH--HOW'S I GET THIS OFF?!
THIS GONNA TAKE A LITTLE THOUGHT.
I IS WILLIN' TO GIVE IT AS LITTLE THOUGHT AS POSSIBLE.
YOU GIT ON T'OTHER SIDE ON HIM ALBERT--- AN' LIFT.
LIFT IT IS!
LIFT!
I IS.
IT'S COMIN'!
HEY! YOU LIFTED THE WRONG PART! JUS' ONLY THE POT... LET US DOWN!
YOU NEVER TOLE ME WHAT PART TO LIFT!

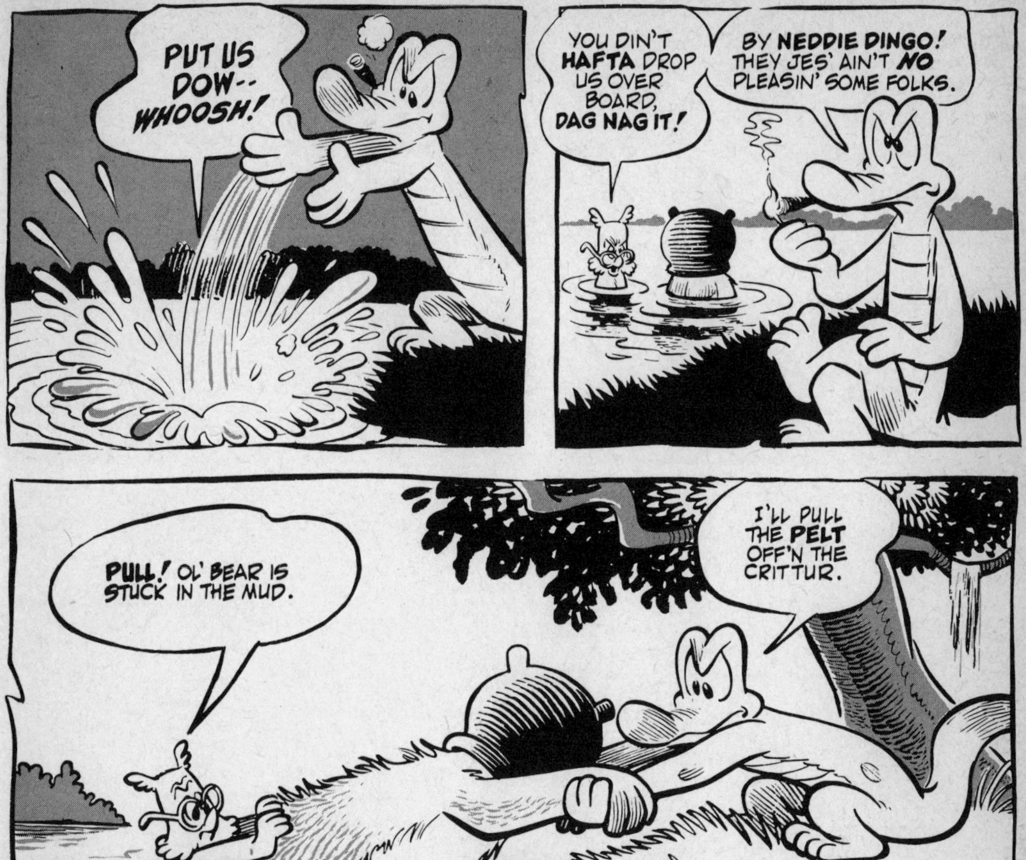
PUT US DOW-- WHOOSH!
YOU DIN'T HAFTA DROP US OVER BOARD, DAG NAG IT!
BY NEDDIE DINGO! THEY JES' AIN'T NO PLEASIN' SOME FOLKS.
PULL! OL' BEAR IS STUCK IN THE MUD.
I'LL PULL THE PELT OFF'N THE CRITTUR.

MY SAKES! WHEN YOU PULLED OUT OL' BEAR, YOU PULLED OFF HIS PANTS!
HE LOOK A LI'L' REE-DICKLEMUST.
OUT OF DECENCY US OUGHT TO DREDGE OUT HIS PANTS.
LET'S NOT BE HASTY... WE IS ALREADY PUT IN A HARD MORNING WORK.
LET US SAUNTER ON HOME FOR LUNCH AFTER WHICH US WILL RETURN WITH PITCHFORKS, CROWBARS AN' MEBBE A LI'L' GUNPOWDER AN' US WILL PRY THE BOY OUTEN THERE!
LIKE THE GOOD NEIGHBORS US IS.
LOOKY THERE, POGO, SOMEBODY WAS FIXIN' TO COOK A GRIZZLE BEAR.
?
WHOEVER PICKED THIS BEAR OUT--PICKED A GOOD ONE-- NICE AN' PLUMP---HOWEVER, YOU NOTICE IT AIN'T BEEN SKUN--- THAT AIN'T HARDLY THE WAY TO COOK A GRIZZLE BEAR.
JES' GIMME A LI'L' BOOSK UP AN' MEBBE I KIN HELP THOSE PEOPLE OUT A LI'L' BIT.

NOW LOAN ME THE BORRY OF YO' **LONGMOLAR.**
IN A MINUTE I'LL HAVE THIS OL' BEAR MOWED CLEAN AS A **NEWBORNT BABE.**
WHAT'S YOU GONE SAY IF THE FOLKS COME BACK FIGGER'N ON EATIN' ***HAIR*** AN' ALL ?
NEXT STEP IN **COOKIN'** THIS BEAR IS TO GIT THE FUR OFFA THE **SIDES**--
HOW WOULD IT BE IF US JES' ***BURNT*** THAT PART OFF ?
IT MIGHT HELP COOK HIM -- AN' GIT HIM **OVERDONE**--*BESIDES THE FOLKS WHAT LEFT HIM HERE MIGHT LIKE **PART** OF HIS HIDE LEFT ON.*
TRUE -- TRUE.
YOU GO RIGHT AHEAD AN' PLAY-- I AIN'T GOT **NO SWEET TOOTH** FOR ***BEAR*** NOHOW.
GOOD-- GUESS I'LL ADD A LI'L' KETCHUP, SOME SALT, A LI'L' MUSTARD AN'-

PLENNY OF PEPPER!
KA-
MY LAND! A PRESSURE COOKER!
CHOO
OH, SOMEBODY ASIDES ME IS GONNA RUE THIS HERE PARTICULAR DAY.
FIGGERIN' OUT HOW TO GIT THE POT OFF?
DOGGONE! IT'S OFF, YOU BULLBAT!

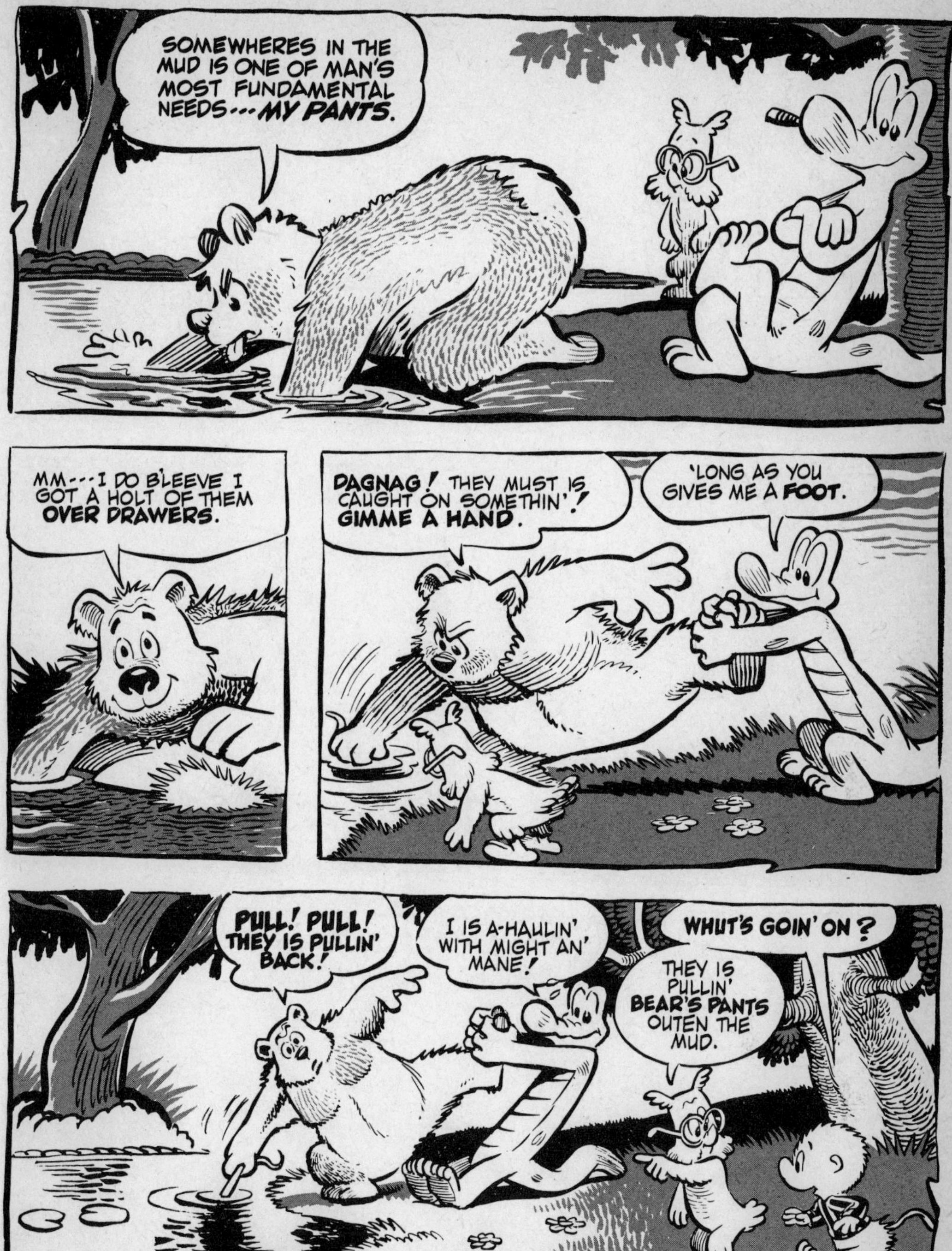

SOMEWHERES IN THE MUD IS ONE OF MAN'S MOST FUNDAMENTAL NEEDS... MY PANTS.
MM--- I DO B'LEEVE I GOT A HOLT OF THEM OVER DRAWERS.
DAGNAG! THEY MUST IS CAUGHT ON SOMETHIN'! GIMME A HAND.
'LONG AS YOU GIVES ME A FOOT.
PULL! PULL! THEY IS PULLIN' BACK!
I IS A-HAULIN' WITH MIGHT AN' MANE!
WHUT'S GOIN' ON?
THEY IS PULLIN' BEAR'S PANTS OUTEN THE MUD.

I SEES SOMETHIN'!
WOOP! THAT WASN'T MY PANTS--!
AN' IT SEES ME.
YOU GOT IT ON ME, YOU GIT IT OFF!
HALP! A RHINOCERWURST IS GOT ALBERT! HALP!

OCTOPOSSIBLE
WOW! HOO BOY! LOOKY HERE NOW! WOWIE!
HAA-HO!
WHAT'S ALL THE FUSS?
YOU'RE THE ONE MAKIN' ALL THE HOOROAR-- --YOU TELL US!
SHUCKS, I JES' SAW A CROWD GATHERIN' AN' FIGGERED I'D DO MY CIVIC DUTY BY WHOOPIN' IT UP FER YA...
OH--WULL, THAT CROWD WAS GATHERIN' TO WATCH OL' BEAR AN' OL' ALBERT RUN OVER THAT WAY.
HOPE YOU DIN'T HURT YOUR THUMB, OLD BOY.

YEP--- OL' BEAR AN' OL' ALBERT RUN OFF WITH A OCTOPUS---
A OCTOPUS!?
YEAH- LOOKY-- I SHOWS YOU HOW THEY DID IT--
SEE --OL' BEAR WAS GOIN' LIKE THIS --- WHEN ALL OVER SUDDEN-- ---HEY-WATCH ME!
DOGGONE, MISTER WEEVIL, IF YOU WANTS TO KNOW WHAT HAPPENS, WATCH ME!
GO AHEAD, DAD----- I'LL KEEP A EYE ON YOU.
ACTUALLY, I DON'T B'LEEVE IN OCTOPUSSES.
WULL-WATCH! I'LL SHOW YOU--- THIS IS HOW THEY DID--- LOOK NOW!
HOW COME YOU DON'T B'LEEVE IN THEM OCTOPUSSES?
I FIGGER THEY IS LEGENDARY BEASTS--
NOW LOOK
NOT MEANIN' NO OFFENSE BUT I THINK UNICORNS, DRAGONS AN' GRYPHONS AN' OCTOPUS IS ALL PRETEND.
OL' BEAR WAS GOIN' LIKE THIS WHEN HE SAY----
WOWF!

HE GOT ME!!
MY SAKES! OWL SURE PUTTIN' ON A REALISTIC SHOW--- NOISE WISE ANYWAY.
HALP!
OCTOPUSSES IS REALLY MYTHOLOGICAL MONSTERS.. NO TWO WAYS 'BOUT IT!
MY LAND, MAN! OWL, YO' HYSTERISICKLE HISTRIONICS IS GONE BE THE DEATH OF YOU SOMEDAY---! DON'T PRETEND SO' REALISTICAL.
CAN'T YOU BELIEVE YOUR EYES?
HOW CAN YOU BELIEVE YOURS WITHOUT NO GLASSES?
YOU MISSED IT! WHAT A SCENE! A OCTOPUS GOT ME!
PHOO! AIN'T NO OCTOPUS IS GOT HIM!
MEBBE HE MEAN A OCTOPUS DID GOT HIM.

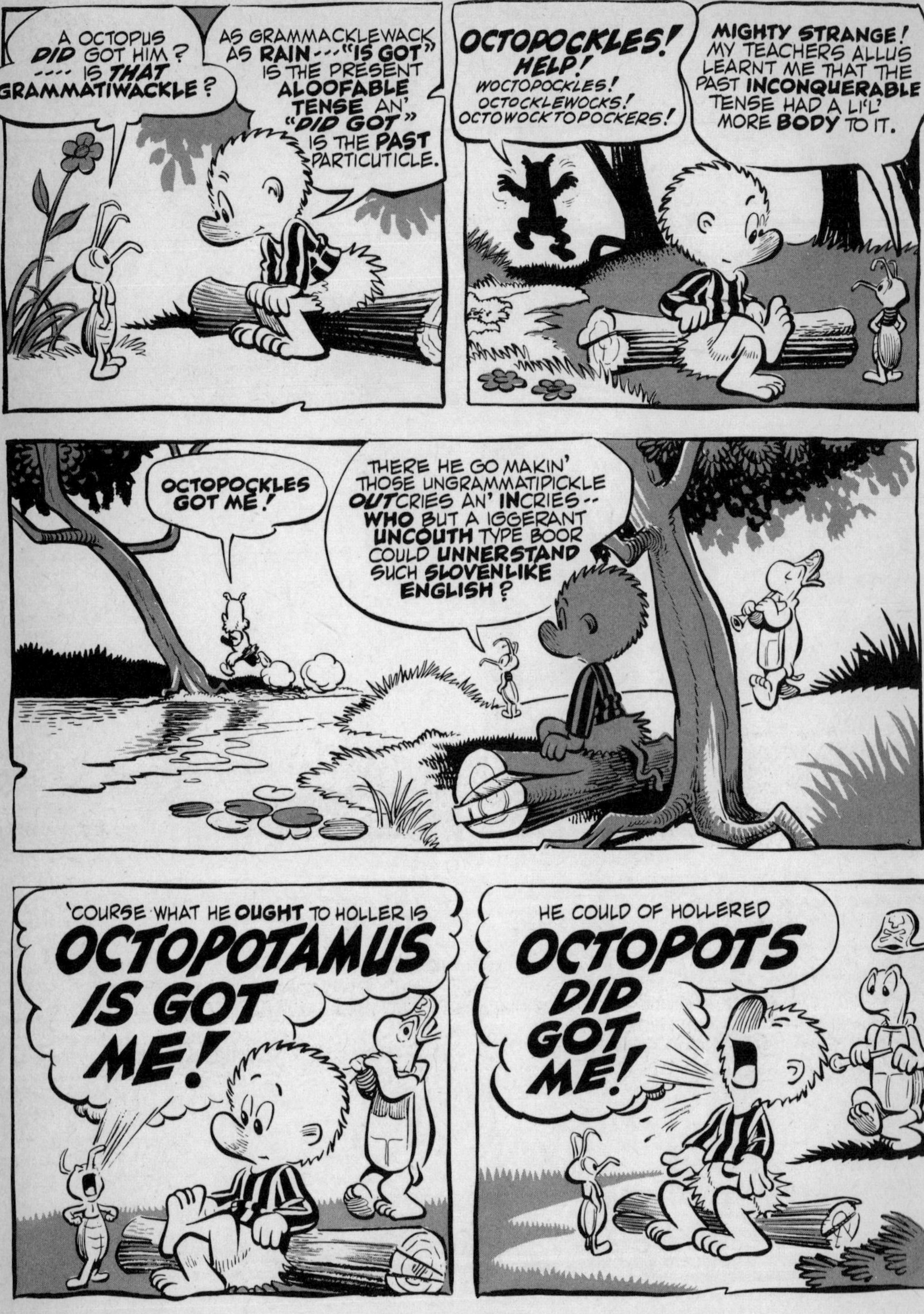
A OCTOPUS DID GOT HIM? ---- IS THAT GRAMMATIWACKLE?
AS GRAMMACKLEWACK AS RAIN---"IS GOT" IS THE PRESENT ALOOFABLE TENSE AN' "DID GOT" IS THE PAST PARTICUTICLE.
OCTOPOCKLES! HELP! WOCTOPOCKLES! OCTOCKLEWOCKS! OCTOWOCKTOPOCKERS!
MIGHTY STRANGE! MY TEACHERS ALLUS LEARNT ME THAT THE PAST INCONQUERABLE TENSE HAD A LI'L' MORE BODY TO IT.
OCTOPOCKLES GOT ME!
THERE HE GO MAKIN' THOSE UNGRAMMATIPICKLE OUTCRIES AN' INCRIES-- WHO BUT A IGGERANT UNCOUTH TYPE BOOR COULD UNNERSTAND SUCH SLOVENLIKE ENGLISH?
'COURSE WHAT HE OUGHT TO HOLLER IS OCTOPOTAMUS IS GOT ME!
HE COULD OF HOLLERED OCTOPOTS DID GOT ME!

THAT'D BE MORE THE PAST INVOKABLE TENSE --ONLY FOR USE 'GAINST ELEPHANT AN' OTHER DRY TYPE GAME.
TRUE.
THEN, IN THAT CASE, HE'D OF HOLLERED ELEPHUMPS DID GOT ME!
WULL I DUNNO.
I'D USE THE PRESENT INDICTIBLE TENSE MORE LIKE THIS ----- RHINOCKWURSTS DONE IS GOT ME!
NO--NO--
THE FUTURE PROVOKABLE WOULD BE BETTER--MORE LIKE HIPPOLOLLIPOPS IS GONE...
BAM
WHAT'S A MATTER? YOU CRAZY OR SOMETHIN'?

WHAT IN THE WORLD IS YOU TWO DOIN'?
STUDYIN' GRAMMAR.
WHERE IS SHE?
OOG!
WE WAS FIGGERIN' OUT WHAT WAS THE PROPER TENSE -- "OOH, A OCTOPUS IS GOT ME" OR "OOH, A OCTOPUS DONE GOT ME!"
EASY.
I WOULD OF HOLLERED -- -- UH -- UH -- UM --
A OCTOPUS DONE GOT ALBERT!
WELL, THAT WOULD BE SAFER -OR MORE GENEROUS I CAN'T FIGGER WHICH.
BUT STILL UNGRAMMATHEMATICAL.

WOWP! A OCTOPOTS IS GOT ALBERT!

OR-- MEBBE IT COULD BE THAT ALBERT IS GOT A OCTOPOTAMUS!

HE MUST OF BEEN MAD AT US, HE NEVER STOPPED TO PASS THE TIME OF DAY---

HE IS FORMED A NEW ATTACHMINT.

YOU MEAN A -- LIKE A NEW ATTACHMINT FOR THE BATHTUB? SOMETHIN' WHAT LETS YOU COOK SHRIMP IN IT AN' TAKE A BATH ALL TO ONCE?

YOU KIN DO THAT ANYWAY-- NO, THIS IS A ATTACHMINT FOR THE OCTOPUS.

WHAT COULD IT BE -- A NINTH LEG?

YES! A NINTH LEG! ONE FOR EACH OF ITS LIFES!

CATS GOT THAT -- NOT OCTOPOCKS.

SERVES ME RIGHT! THIS IS WHAT I GET FOR SHOWIN' UP IN THE SUNDAY FUNNIES-- SHOULD BE IN SUNDAY SCHOOL.

FIGMENTALITY

DOGGONE ALBERT, IS YOU GOT A OCTOPUS OR IS IT GOT YOU?

SON, I IS BECOMED CONVINCED IT'S JUS' A THING OF THE MIND---A FIGMENT.

NAME OF NEWTON?

HOWDY, NEWT.

GUNK

GUNK

I IS SO WORED OUT RUNNIN' FROM IT, I IS DECIDED TO LIVE WITH IT.

COULDN'T YOU COMB IT OUTEN YO' HAIR?

GUNK

BY JING, YOU IS BEGINNIN' TO LOOK LIKE YOU ENJOYS LIVIN' DOWNSTAIRS FROM A OCTOPUS.
I TELL YOU, POGO, 'TAINT EVER'BODY GOT A OCTOPUS.
AN' UP TO NOW, THAT HAS BEEN 'A JIM-DANDY A-RRANGEMINTS.
PHOO! YOU IS JES' JEALOUS 'CAUSE YOU ISN'T GOT ONE OF THESE HANDY GADGETS AS A AID AN' COMFORT IN YO' OLD AGE ---
FOR THE LIFE OF ME, ALBERT, I CAN'T FIGGER WHY ANYBODY'D WANNA KEEP A OCTOPUS.
YOU JES' AIN'T GOT NO IMAGINATION--- MIGHT COME A DAY THE OCTOPUS WOULD KEEP YOU!
THE KATHRYN BARBARA

THAT'S ONE OF YO' MORE REE-DICKLEMOST REMARKS..
AN' A TIP OF THE OCTOPUS HAT TO YOU, SIR.
WHY WOULD A OCTOPUS WANT TO KEEP ME?
MEBBE AS A CURIO -- OR SOMETHIN' TO ENLIVEN SUNDAY AFTERNOONS..
THE KATHRYN BARBARA
WULL, I IS PERTY LIVELY ON SUNDAY AFTERNOONS WHAT WITH SINGIN' SONGS AN' VISITIN' THEM AS GOT THE MISERABLES...
MEBBE BEIN' AS WE IS IN THE DULL PART OF THE DULLDRUMS YOU COULD RIFF OFF A SMALL OBLIGOTTIO RIGHT NOW?
GLAD TO.. MM
MI-MI-MI-HUM
THE KATHRYN BARBARA
WHOO-HOO-HUM
DEE DUM
BEE-HOLE! LOOKY THERE, MERTON, A GONDOLIA AN' A GONDOLIATOR SINGIN' TO A MERMAID!
THE KATHRYN BARBARA
I AIN'T NEITHER NO MOOR-MAID!

AAH! DESTROY A SON'S FAITH IN HIS FATHER, WILL YOU!? PELT HIM, GROTON! PELT HIM!
WHO'S YOUR FRIENDS?
SUNDAY DRIVER TYPES.
KATHRYN BARBARA
HERE'S A BIG ONE, DAD.
THEY PROB'LY DIDN'T GOT A LICENSE FER THAT ANYWAY.
YOU CAN'T TRUST LEGENDARY MONSTERS AN' MYTHICAL BEASTS, BUNSTON.
THEY AIN'T NOTHIN' COOLER NOR HAVIN' A OCTOPUS ON YO' HEAD, POGO.
BESIDES IT GIVE A MAN A ROMANTICAL LOOK-- MAKE HIM 'PEAR TO HAVE A NATURAL-BORN HEAD OF NATURAL-BORN WAVY-TYPE HAIR.
WEARIN' A OCTOPUS THIS WAY, WHAT BE-LOVED HISTORIWOCKAL CHARACTER DO I RE-MIND YOU OF?
"BE-LOVED?"
OF COURSE "BE-LOVED." WHAT ELSE WOULD A TRUE BLUE ALLIGATOR BE?
LEMME THINK.

THINK AWAY... SEE IF YOU KIN GUESS WHO I IS..
WHO? HUM DEE DUM..
I KIN TELL YOU IT AIN'T HUM DEE DUM...
NOSSIR, IT AIN'T NO MOTHER GOOSERY RHYME CHARACTER.
LESSEE.. WHAT BEE-LOVED HIS-TORICAL CHARACTER DO YOU REEMIND ME OF?
YOU'LL NEVER GUESS.
YOWTCH!
BY JING! IF YOU GONNA LIVE UPSTAIRS YOU GOTTA BUY YO' OWN SEE-GARS.
I GOT IT! YOU RE-MIND ME OF COUSIN ANNIE PROUDFOOTS WHAT GOT HER HEAD CAUGHT IN A CAN OF BAIT.

A GOOD SPOT FOR A DOG

"HOW COME YOU ACTIN' SO **FRIENDLY**---? IT SORTA **SKEER** ME."

"ON ACCOUNT I IS PERSONAL FOND OF YOU AN' BESIDES I GOIN' INTO **BUSINESS** WITH YOU."

"LAST TIME I WAS IN BUSINESS WITH **YOU** YOU WAS S'POSE TO **ADVISE** ME -- AN' YOU GOT ME INTO A FIGHT WITH A **BEAR**."

"TRUE."

"AN' WHEN I SAW THE WAY THINGS WAS GOIN' -- **WHAT** DID I ADVISE YOU TO DO?"

"I DUNNO -- WHAT **WAS** YO' ADVICE?"

"**RUN!** I SAID -- THAT'S WHAT I SAID"

"I TELL YOU, I IS A **NATURAL BORN ADVISOR** -- WHAT BETTER ADVICE COULD YOU GIT IN A BEAR FIGHT THAN TO RUN FER HOME?"

"WITH THE BEAR **AFTER** YOU?"

Panel 1:
— CERT'LY -- YOU WOONENT WANT IT TO GIT THERE AFORE YOU, WOULD YOU?
— YOU'RE SUCH A GOOD ADVISOR WHAT'D YOU TELL OL' ALBERT THERE TO DO?

Panel 3:
MY LAND! I DON'T SEE ALBERT... BUT I'D ADVISE THAT YOUNG WOMAN OUT THERE TO GIVE UP SEE-GARS -- IT'S UNCOUTH!

Panel 4:
— THAT AIN'T UNCOUTH! THAT'S ALBERT!
— BY JING! HE LOOK LIKE A SIGH-REEN!

Panel 5:
— YOU MEAN ONE OF THEM THINGS WHAT SIT ON THE FRONT OF A FIRE ENGINE?
— NOPE...ONE OF THEM CRITTURS WHAT USED TO LURK IN THE LEGENDARY ISLANDS AN' LURED SAILORS TO THEY DEATHS.

Panel 6:
— I COMES FROM A SEA-FARIN' FAMBLY -- HE GOT SOME NERVE -- HE'S A BEAST!
— THAT'S WHAT HE LOOKS LIKE.

YOO HOO, FELLOWS.
WHO'S THE LI'L' BUM WHAT HIT ME ON THE OCTOPUS WITH THAT CLUMMOCK?
YOU GOTTA ADMIT IT WAS A GOOD SHOT.
SOME LURE! WHOOSH! HE GOT A VOICE LIKE UNTO A BULL-BURGLAR.
DON'T KNOW WHY I ALLUS GOTTA WASH OUT THE OCTOPUSH.
ANYBODY WHAT HITS ME ON THE OCTOPUS GOT A LIFE-TIME FEUD ON HIS HANDS AN' THEM TWO IS DONE DID IT AN' SO DONE GOT IT.
BUT THEY IS BEIN' REASONABLE--- THEY IS OFFERIN' YOU DAMAGES.
YOO HOO YOO HOO YOO HOO YOO HOO YOO HOO YOO HOO YOO HOO HOO HOO HA HO HOO HA.
HELLO HELLO
CAP'N P. SCHWED

PHOO! THEY ALREADY GIMME DAMAGES--- THEY PUT A DENT IN MY NEW OCTOPUS AN' HIT ME IN THE EYEBONE WITH A LUNK OF SWAMP TUNDRA.
HA! WHAT CAN THEY DO TO REPAY ME!? -- I'LL NEVER SPEAK TO 'EM IN MY LIFE -- THEY TREATED MY OCTOPUS LIKE A BROTHER-IN-LAW -- EVEN MONEY CANNOT CHANGE ME!
HE SAY HE DON'T WANT YO' DIRTY OL' MILLION DOLLARS.
PETER SCHWED
I DON'T WANT WHAT?!
EVIDENTLY WE IS ONLY SUCCEEDED IN INSULTIN' HIM.
MONEY CAN'T SWAY YOU, LIKE YOU SAID.
THERE -- THERE! YOU DIN'T MEAN NO HARM --- YOU JES' WANTED TO SET HIM UP IN BUSINESS AS A SIGH-REEN ENTICIN' SAILORS TO OUR ISLAND ON WHICH WE'D SELL 'EM HOT DOGS AN' ALL -- WE WAS READY TO SPLIT OUR FIRST TWO MILLION WITH HIM.
POGO, YOU DID ME OUT OF A MODEST FORTUNE --- HEY! COME BACK!
HE'S AROUSED!
RUN! RUN! WE IS WOUNDED HIS FIERCE ALLIGATOR PRIDE BY TALKIN' OF TAWDRY MONEY! DON'T LET HIM GIT YOU!
AARGH!

DUCK INTO YO' HOUSE HERE, OWL, AN' CLAIM US AIN'T HOME!
HEY---COME BACK!
NOBODY AIN'T HOME!
IS YOU SURE? I JES' SAW SOMEBODY GO IN.
THERE AIN'T NOBODY HERE BUT ME AN' MY BEAUTIFUL DAUGHTER.
PHOO! YOU IS SKEERIN' MY OCTOPUS.
I DEE-MANDS TO KNOW WHERE'S THE MILLION DOLLARS YOU IS OFFERED ME?
STEP RIGHT IN! WE'S GONE SET YOU UP AS A SIGH-REEN BLOWIN' A BUGLE AN' SELLIN' HOT DOGS.
GOOD--- WAIT'LL I TAKES OFF MY OCTOPUS.
WATCH--- LIKE THIS.

86

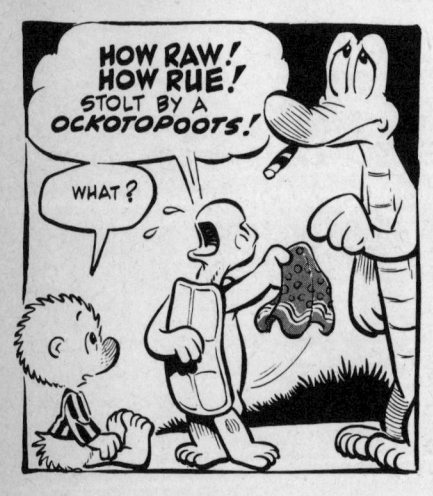

HOW SADFUL AND SORROWBLE! ---OWL KIDNAPPERED BY A OCTOPOOSE!
BEHOLT! THE PRODIGOGGLE OWL IS RETURNIN'!
IF HE GOT THE OCTOCKOPOT WITH HIM, I IS GOT A DATE IN TENNESSEE---
COME BACK HERE---OWL IS ALONE.
OWL--! I WAS JES' ABOUT TO ORGANIZE A SAFARI TO SEARCH YOU OUT AN' SAVE YO' NATURAL BORN SKIN!
MY SKIN?
SURE, YO' SKIN!--- THEN IN CASE YO' WAS KILT US COULD STUFF YO' SKIN WITH STUFFIN' AN' PRESERVE YOU FOR POSTERITY.
YOU IS A TRUE FRIEND.
WHAT FLAVOR STUFFIN'?
OH--MEBBE LICORICE, PEANER BUTTER, LEMON MACRANG, OR CHICKEN FOOT---
YOU IS TRUE AND BLUE.
HEY, DOGGONE! HOW'D YOU GIT AWAY?

WULL, FIRST I PUT UP A TERRIBOBBLE STRUGGLE--- THOUSANDS OF OCTOPOOT GROSPED AT ME BUT I FIT 'EM OFF!
THERE HE IS NOW! COME BACK HERE, SPOT, DON'T YOU KNOW YO' OWN LI'L' MASTERS?
MASTERS? YOU FROGS IS HIS MASTERS?
SURE! US TRADED A SNAKE AN' TWO SNAILS TO A OCTOPUS FER HIM. HE'S OUR PET--COME ON HOME, SPOT-- US GOT A HAM BONE FOR YOU, SPOT.
WULL -- HE'LL MAKE A GOOD BIRD DOG.
THAT'S A GOOD ONE, SIR.
HERE'S YO' COLLAR, SPOT -- COME ON, BOY.
FAIR IS FAIR, SPOT.
WHY IS YOU CALLIN' MY OLD FRIEND HOWLAND OWL SUCH A NAME AS SPOT?
THEY COULD OF CALLED HIM "ROVER" OR PERHAPS "ETHELBERT"--- US HAD A DOG NAME OF THAT ONE TIME-- --AND WAS HE MAD!--HATED THE NAME! JOINED THE NAVY, FINELY.
WHAT ELSE YOU GONE CALL A DOG?

HE WAS A CARROT HOUND. HE CAUGHT A ONION ONE NIGHT THINKIN' IT WAS A CARROT... BOY, IT BRUNG TEARS TO HIS EYES WHEN HE SEEN HIS MISTAKE. HE WAS A PROUD BEAST.
HOW KIN A DOG HAVE FEATHERS?
THE WONDERS OF NATURE AIN'T MINE TO QUESTION, FRIEND.
I IS UGLY WHEN I IS RILED, LI'L' SIRS.
COME TO THINK OF IT, YOU IS UGLY UNRILED TOO.
IF HE'S A DOG WHERE'S YO' DOG LICENSE?
YOU IS A ALLIGATOR! WHERE'S YO' ALLIGATOR LICENSE?
AARGH!
ALBERT IS OUT-THINKIN' 'EM NOW.
YOU COULD BE THROWN NINETY YEARS INTO COLD STORAGE FER PRACTICIN' WITHOUT A LICENSE.
WHY, YOU LI'L' FAT LONG LEGGED OYSTERS--
SNAP
I AIN'T PRACTICIN'! ROWR!
RUN, SAM! NEXT TIME WE GITS A DOG MAKE IT A GRIZZLE-BEAR.
YOU KNOW, NOBODY NEVER DID 'SPLAIN HOW A DOG COULD HAVE FEATHERS.
HATS HAVE 'EM, PILLOWS, INDIANS, WHY NOT DOGS?

Really Round the Ragboys

Hobble the goblins
And rabble the rouse
Weary the Willie
And homily house
All of the Pollys
The Annas demand;
Deliver the liverty,
Bellow the Bland.

A Tuppenny Thrupence

Please plorridge hlot!
Please plorridge clold!
Please plorridge in the plot,
Nline dlays lold.

Our Colander is Full of Holes

The Firth of Forth
Lithe in the north,
The first of course
Comes 'fore the fourth
And after fourth is fifth,
Befourth, of course,
Forsooth the sixth;
With tooth and thirth
Somewheres betwixth
July the Forth and Firth.

A GREAT IDEA

This idea of mine is a ring-tailed doozy.

All yo' ideas is ring-tailed somethin' or others.

Out of courtesy to me I will IGNORE that-- where at is the lunch?

The lunch is jes' EGG-zackly where it BEE-longs.

Namely WHERE?

Namely INSIDE of ME.

I got up afore breakfast an' DISPOSED of it.

Right over there is my great idea--- a machine to take you to CHINA!

OL' SECKERTARY OF STATE KNOW 'BOUT THIS ?
THERE YOU IS ... YOU POINTS IT STRAIGHT DOWN AND STARTS --AND ERE LONG YOU IS IN HONG KONG!
IS ERE LONG LIKE OO LONG ?
HOW WILL THIS HERE NOW MACHINE TAKE ANYBODY ALL THE WAY TO CHINA ?
BUY A TICKET AN' I TELLS YOU.
'FORE I'D USE YOUR TYPE OF BRAINS HERE, I'D USE MY OWN..
YOU IS FORGITTIN' THAT I IS IN CHARGE OF THIS HERE MACHINE.
YOU LOOKS LIKE A OLD SHOVELER AT THAT.
I'LL FIGGER THIS OUT SINGLE BRAINED..
STOP! DEE-SIST! CEASE!

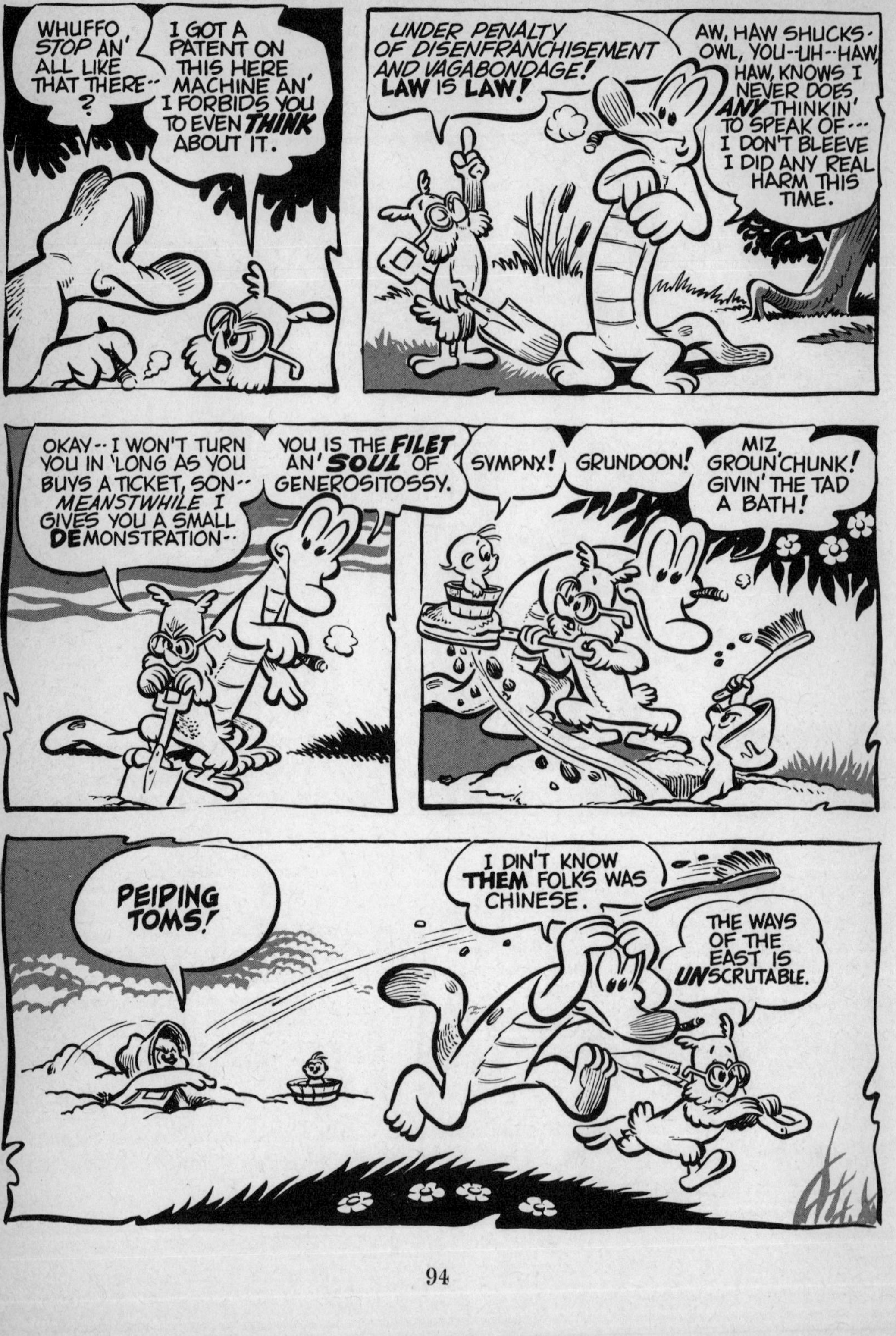
WHUFFO STOP AN' ALL LIKE THAT THERE-- ?
I GOT A PATENT ON THIS HERE MACHINE AN' I FORBIDS YOU TO EVEN THINK ABOUT IT.
UNDER PENALTY OF DISENFRANCHISEMENT AND VAGABONDAGE! LAW IS LAW!
AW, HAW SHUCKS-OWL, YOU--UH--HAW, HAW, KNOWS I NEVER DOES ANY THINKIN' TO SPEAK OF--- I DON'T BLEEVE I DID ANY REAL HARM THIS TIME.
OKAY-- I WON'T TURN YOU IN 'LONG AS YOU BUYS A TICKET, SON-- MEANSTWHILE I GIVES YOU A SMALL DEMONSTRATION--
YOU IS THE FILET AN' SOUL OF GENEROSITOSSY.
SYMPNX!
GRUNDOON!
MIZ GROUN'CHUNK! GIVIN' THE TAD A BATH!
PEIPING TOMS!
I DIN'T KNOW THEM FOLKS WAS CHINESE.
THE WAYS OF THE EAST IS UNSCRUTABLE.

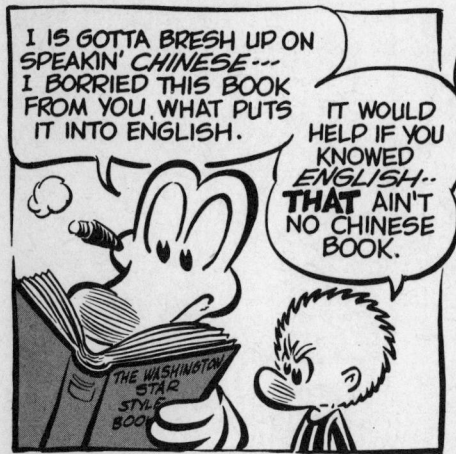

A DILLER A DULLARD A TEN O'CLOCK SKULLER

"HARD FO' ME TO B'LEEVE **YOU'D** RUTHER READ THAN GO FISHIN', ALBERT."

"I IS GOTTA BRESH UP ON SPEAKIN' *CHINESE*--- I BORRIED THIS BOOK FROM YOU, WHAT PUTS IT INTO ENGLISH."

"IT WOULD HELP IF YOU KNOWED *ENGLISH*-- **THAT** AIN'T NO CHINESE BOOK."

THE WASHINGTON STAR STYLE BOOK

"LOOKS PERTY ***DOGGONE CHINESEY* TO ME!** CAN'T I LEARN NO ORIENTAL TONGUE FROM THIS'N AT ALL?"

"WELL-- **HARDLY** ANY."

"WHAT INNERESTIN' AN' FASCINATIN' DOIN'S IS YOU RASCALS UP TO?"

"**ALBERT** GONE GO TO **CHINA**-- HE BEEN STUDYIN' UP THE LANGUAGE."

"AN' SO IT'S **FAREWELL!** I IS GONE OVER AN' SEE OWL TO BUY MY TICKET."

96

HOW COME THEY CALLS IT THE INDIAN OCEAN...? IS IT FULL OF SIOUX?
NO, I BELIEVE IT GOT SOMETHIN' TO DO WITH THE CLEVELAND BASEBALL CLUB.
THE FITZPATRICK

HE GONNA GET HIS FEET WET ALL THE WAY OVER HIS HEAD.
OL' OWL IS TALKED HIM INTO IT--LITTLE DOES THEY KNOW THAT DIRECT THRU THE WORLD IS THE OCEAN AN' NOT CHINA!
THE DANIEL FITZPATRICK

AN' JUST THINK! IF HE BORES A HOLE FROM OUR SIDE RIGHT THRU THE EARTH AND INTO THE INDIAN OCEAN, LIKE AS NOT THE OCEAN WILL POUR THRU THE HOLE AND DEE-LUGE US ALL!
IF IT'S FOREIGN WATER IT'LL GOTTA GIT PAST THE IMMIGRATION OFFICE AND THE TARIFF PEOPLE!
THE DANIEL FITZPATRICK

98

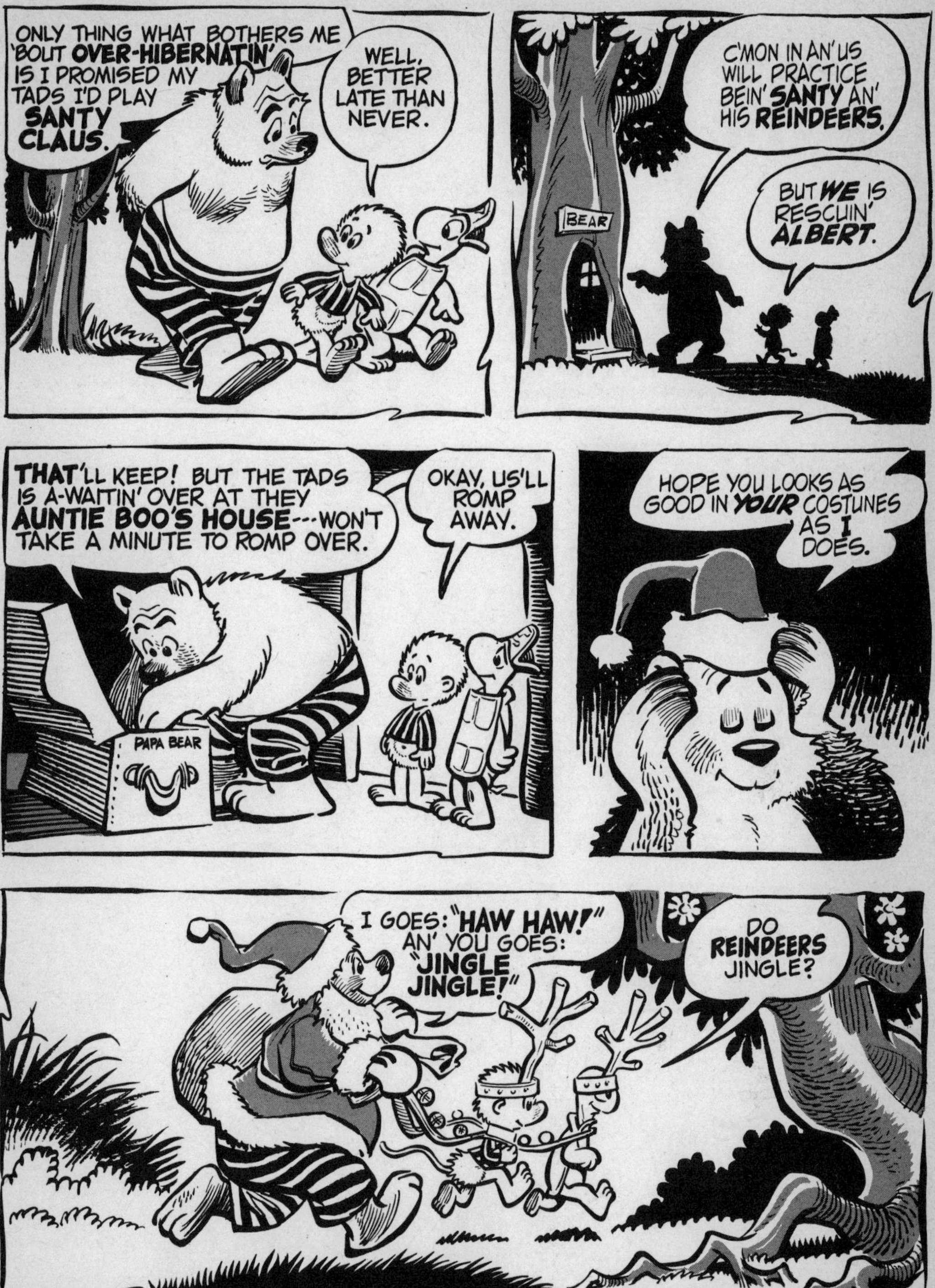
ONLY THING WHAT BOTHERS ME 'BOUT OVER-HIBERNATIN' IS I PROMISED MY TADS I'D PLAY SANTY CLAUS.
WELL, BETTER LATE THAN NEVER.
C'MON IN AN' US WILL PRACTICE BEIN' SANTY AN' HIS REINDEERS.
BEAR
BUT WE IS RESCUIN' ALBERT.
THAT'LL KEEP! BUT THE TADS IS A-WAITIN' OVER AT THEY AUNTIE BOO'S HOUSE---WON'T TAKE A MINUTE TO ROMP OVER.
OKAY, US'LL ROMP AWAY.
PAPA BEAR
HOPE YOU LOOKS AS GOOD IN YOUR COSTUNES AS I DOES.
I GOES: "HAW HAW!" AN' YOU GOES: "JINGLE JINGLE!"
DO REINDEERS JINGLE?

A DEEP IN THE SLEEP
SEEM LIKE SOMEBODY'S FOLLOWIN' US.
LOOK AN' SEE... AIN'T GONE TAKE ANYBODY TO CHINA, FREE.
NOBODY!
HOOTCHIE
KOOTCHIE KOO
STOP TALKIN' BABY TALK.
WELL, HERE WE GO TO CHINA.
HOLD TIGHT! THE HONK KONG EXPRESS IS LEAVIN'.
THE HONG KONG EXPRESS IS A SHOVEL?
YEP... THE SPADE-NIK!

HOW KIN YOU TELL WHERE YOU WILL COME OUT ?
S'POSE US WANTED TO GO TO SHANGHAI?
YEAH! AN' YOU BRUNG US OUT IN CANTON!
OR PEKING!
I'LL BRING YOU OUT IN SING SING IF YOU ISN'T CAREFUL.
S'POSE INSTEAD OF COMIN' OUT IN CHINA LIKE YOU SAYS, YOU COMES OUT IN SIBERIA!
IN A SALT MINE!
HOT DOG! I LOVES SALT--- WITH CORN ON THE COB.
OR SALT WITH FRYIN' EGGS.
OR SALT ON PORK CHOMPS.
OR SALT ON CELERARY AN' REDDISHES.
TROUBLE IS YOU AIN'T GONE HAVE NOTHIN' TO PUT SALT ON 'CEPT SALT!
OR ON EACH OTHER.
US COULD ALWAYS GO TO THE CORNER GROCERARY STORE.
SURE, AN' US COULD BUY A REDDISH OR A CELERARY.

WHAT WOULD YOU USE FOR MONEY?
US WOULD SELL YOU BOTH TO A JUNK DEALER.
`COURSE WE WOULDN'T GIT MUCH--- I B'LEEVE IT'S FORTY-SEVEN KULAKS TO THE DOLLAR NOW.
WE DEMAND OUR FARE MONEY BACK!
WE AIN'T GOIN'!
YOU AIN'T NEVER BOUGHT NO TICKETS -- BUT I'LL GIVE YOU SOMETHIN'--
QUICK! HEAD FOR THE CAPITOL -- WE IS UNCOVERED A UNDER-GROUND PLOT!
MERRY CHRISTMAS TO ALL AND TO ALL A GOOD NIGHT!
JINGLE.
JINGLE.
GOOD NIGHT IS A UNDER STATEMINTS.
IS WE IN CHINA ALREADY? --- THEY HAS A EARLY CHRISTMAS HERE.
OR A LATE ONE.
HAW HAW HAW
JINGLE!
JINGLE!

Panel 1: "THAT SANDY CLAWS WE SAW HAD ON STRIPEY PANTS--- LIKE UNTO A CONVICT!" "FOLKS IN THE DIPLOMATIC SERVICES WEARS STRIPEY PANTS AN' VERY FEW OF 'EM IS CONVICTS."

Panel 2: "HOWEVER---IF WE IS COME OUT IN CHINA ALREADY--- MEBBE THEY IS PUT SANDY CLAWS IN JAIL!"

Panel 3: "MEBBE THEM BUGS WAS RIGHT-- WE IS COME OUT IN SIBERIA!" "IF SO SIBERIA LOOK MITEY FRIEN'LY-- LIKE GEORGIA."

Panel 4: "DOES YOU REALIZE THAT GEORGIA IS PART OF THE ROOSIAN UMPIRE?"

Panel 5: "BY BILLY RAY! I'LL GIT A BOOK OF MAPS AN' PROVE IT TO YOU." "'COURSE I DON'T SEE HOW WE COULD OF GONE ANY WHERES-- I IS ONLY DUG DOWN 'BOUT TWO FOOTS."

Panel 6: "THERE!-- THERE IS BALL-FACED PROOF!" (book: MAPS PUZZLES AND MAGIC TRICKS)

SEE! GEORGIA IS PART OF THE U.S.S.R.
WHOOIE! DO YO'S'POSE SANDY CLAWS IS ON THEIR SIDE?
YOU FIGGER THEM BOLSHEVINKS CREPT UP AN' STOLT THE STATE?
THEY MUST OF IS DO.
MAPS PUZZLES AND OTHER MAGIC TRICKS
BY NAB! THEY GOT A NERVE!
YOU GOT A SOAPBOX ON YOU? I WANTS TO MAKE A SPEECH!
WE GOT NO TIME TO LOSE -- US IS GOTTA STEAL BACK THE STATE!
RIGHT! YOU JES' KEEP YO' ARMS OUT AN' I'LL FILL YOU UP--- THEN US WILL CRAWL BACK THRU THE HOLE!
BEARIN' OUR BELOVED SWAMP IN OUR ARMS!
US BETTER HURRY UP--- TAKE 'S MUCH 'S WE CAN.

I'LL BE DOGBONED IF THEM LI'L' TOVAROOCHES ISN'T STOLT OWL, TOO!
?
I DIN'T SEE THE EARLY PART OF THE SHOW; JES' CAME IN---WHAT'S GOIN' ON, FRIEND ?
WHERE IS YOU FROM, MR. HORNER?
I IS FROM OVER AT FARGO.
IT'S GOOD TO SEE A BOY FROM OVER AT HOME-- ---WE GONE HAVE TROUBLE GITTIN' THE STATE BACK INTO THE U.S. AND A.
HUH?
ME AN' OWL DUG A HOLE THRU THE EARTH, COME OUT IN ROOSIA AN', BEHOLD, THEM BOLSHEVIKS HAD STOLED OUR SOVEREIGN STATE OF GEORGIA--- THERE IT WAS PLAIN AS MUD ...
NEXT THING I KNEWED OWL HAD VANISHED AN'-
LISTEN! YOU AIN'T IN RUSSIA--- THIS IS ALL A BAD DREAM--- YOU'RE HOME IN THE SWAMP---

GEE THANKS FOR STRAIGHTEN ME OUT.
NOW YOU CAN GO HOME AN' GIT A GOOD NIGHT'S SLEEP.
OFF WE GO!
JES' A DOGBONE MINUTE! SOMEBODY GOTTA CRAWL BACK THRU THAT HOLE AN' BRING OWL BACK FROM RUSSIA TOO.
ALBERT, YOU IS CRAZY FOR THINKIN' YOU AN' OWL TUNNELED THRU THE EARTH AN' WOUND UP IN ROOSIA!
FOLKS LAUGHED AT FULTON, TOO.
NO WONDER! HIM AN' HIS FISH MARKET. ----- LOOK! THIS PLACE IS GEORGIA!
GEORGIA, U.S.S.R.
EVERYBODY KNOW GEORGIA IS IN THE UNITE AN' STATES.
US GOT A BOOK OF MAPS WHAT PROVE THE U.S.S.R. GOT A GEORGIA TOO! THE SAME ONE!

THEY STOLT IT!
I REPEAT, ALBERT, YOU IS LOOSE IN THE FLUE!
THAT PROVE IT! YOU IS A SPY! YOU IS A DISLOYAL TOVAROOTCH---YOU BUM! BACK TO THE GREMLIN!
CAREFUL! IT'S BAD LUCK TO SKOOSH A BUG----- 'SPECIALLY A HORNET! WE GITS RAIN.
OH, THE DUPLICITY OF MANKIND---AN' BUGKIND---RUNNIN' OFF AN' LEAVIN' ME TO FILL UP THAT HOLE BY MYSELF ---AN' LEAVIN' ME TO FIND OWL BY MYSELF!
BUT I IS A TRUE FRIEND EVER WILLIN' TO SACK-OR-FICE MYSELF - KINDLY CORNSIDERATE AN' GENTLERUST TO A FAULT!
AN' THE FAULT IS YOURS, SIR - GIT OFFA MY SHOVEL YOU BUM - AN' STOP HEAVYIN' UP THE LOAD!
BUT IT'S ME! YOUR BELOVED FRIEND, ME, OWL! FOUND!
YOU MAY KISS MY HAND.

TWO THREE MINUTE HEADS

IT MAKE MY BLOOD BOIL!

I NEVER HAD SUCH A HARROWIN' EXPERIENCE.

HOW DO THESE REEVOLUTIONARIES THINK THEY GONE GIT AWAY WITH COVER'N UP A HARMLESS (THO' STUPID) CITIZEN --- NAMELY YOU, WITH DIRT.

A EXCELLENT SUMMATION.

HOWEVER.. THEY DIN'T DO IT.

WHO DID, IF THEM DIN'T DIN IT?

WAIT'LL I WINDS UP.

YOU DID!

OWL, YOU IS UNDER THE INFLOONCE OF A HYPERNOTICKAL SPELL--THEM BOLSHEVINKS IS MADE YOU THINK I IS RESPONSIBLE FOR YOU BEIN' BURIED ALIVE!
BESIDES I SAW YOU DO IT.
SAW ME?!
NOW I SEES THRU YOUR GAME--HOW COULD YOU SEE ME IF YOU WAS BURIED? YOU BURIED YOURSELF SO AS TO PUT THE BLAME ON ME!
WOWF!
YOU WOWFED AT ME! ---THEY IS NO SENSE IN LOSIN' YO' TEMPER, SON.
GAMBER WAZZLE! GAMBER WAZZLE!
BEHOLD! SANTY CLAUS IS CAPTURED TWO OF OUR AIRCRAFT!
JINGLE
JOYEUX NOEL!

SANDY CLAUS IS TURNED! THEM ROOSIANS IS STOLT EVERYTHING SACRED! OUR HOUSES WITH LI'L LUNCHES --- ALL!
NOTHIN' TO DO BUT GO TO POGO'S PLACE FOR COOKIES AN' SAM-WICHES AN' FIGGER THIS OUT.
WELL-SANDY ON THEIR SIDE! US COULD TAKE A RADICAL STEP! WE KIN BOYCOTT THE WHOLE IDEA-- REFUSE TO HANG UP OUR STOCKIN'S.
WE'LL KEEP THE OLD NOODLE SHARP WITH FOOD!
RIGHT! THEN OUR MASSIVE INTELLIGENCE WILL RETALIATE RIGHT UP TO THE BRINK.
HOORAY! IT'S GRUNDOON!
SKBZFG!
IT'S GRUNDOON ALL RIGHT, BUT WHAT'S SO ALL FIRED HOORAY ABOUT THAT?
KTPV?

COME TO THINK OF IT - WHAT IS SO HOORAY?
HE'S A GOOD KID BUT HE BITES-- FOLKS DON'T EXACT BREAK OUT IN CHEERS WHEN YOU RUSHES IN SAYIN'--
MKRNTZ.
WHY, BLESS MY EVER-LOVIN' BLUE EYED SELF IF IT AIN'T GRUNDOON!
ZSMPNTK?
OW!
SNOP
SEEIN' GRUNDOON ENJOYIN' YOUR FINGER REMINDS ME WE IS ON OUR WAY TO EATS.
HOW KIN I BE SO BRAINLESS WHEN I IS SO SMART?

REINDEER DON'T REIN IN VAIN, DEAR

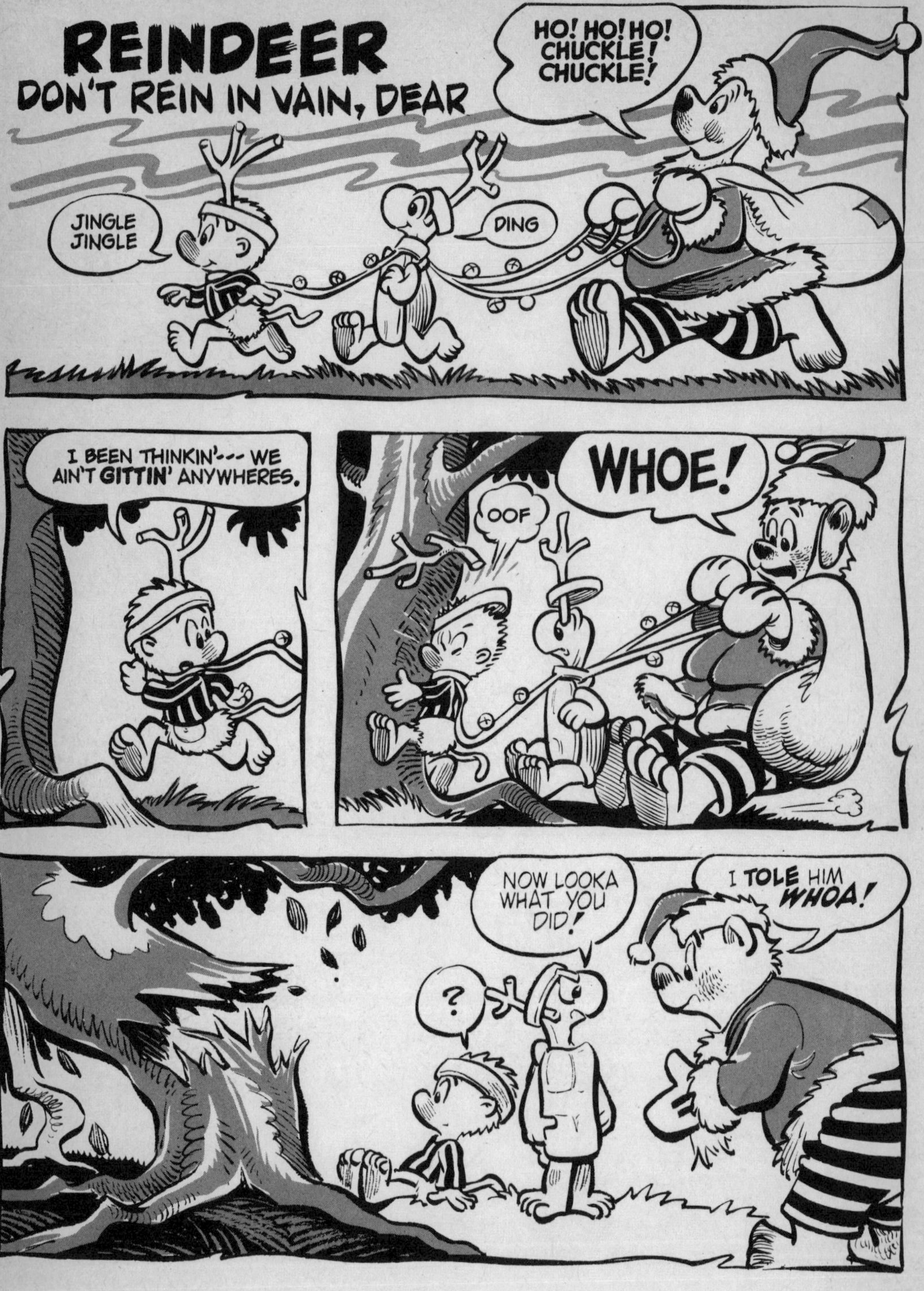

I DON'T ENJOY BEING DRIV INTO TREES... --I RESIGN!
IN THAT CASE, I APPOINTS YOU HEAD REINDEER.
OH BOY.
OH, YUM YUM YUM! THANK YOU, KIND SIR! I IS RIZ TO THE TOP OF MY CALLING AN' ME SO YOUNG.
NOW, NOW, STOP BUTTERING UP THE BOSS... JUS' DO YOUR REINDEERIN' WITH PRIDE.
OH, I AM PROUD.
I WANTS REINDEERS WHAT IS PROUD AND MANLY, LIGHT OF FOOT, QUICK OF EYE.
I'LL BE PROUD IF YOU'LL BE MANLY, STANLEY.
IN MY DAY REINDEERS WAS SPRY.
SPRY AND NIMBLE... DAINTY AND QUICK!

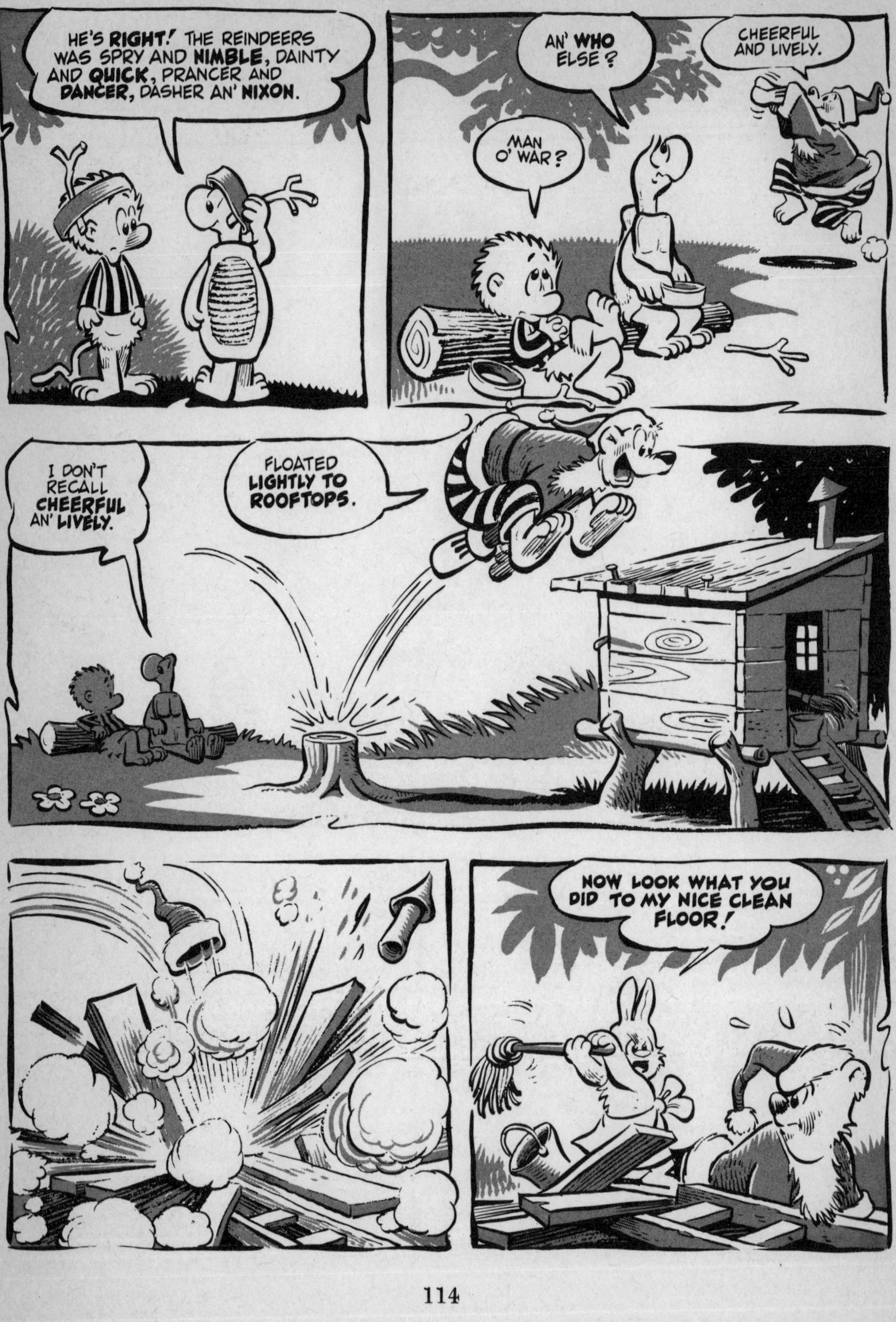
HE'S RIGHT! THE REINDEERS WAS SPRY AND NIMBLE, DAINTY AND QUICK, PRANCER AND DANCER, DASHER AN' NIXON.
AN' WHO ELSE?
CHEERFUL AND LIVELY.
MAN O' WAR?
I DON'T RECALL CHEERFUL AN' LIVELY.
FLOATED LIGHTLY TO ROOFTOPS.
NOW LOOK WHAT YOU DID TO MY NICE CLEAN FLOOR!

YOU MENS IS ALL ALIKE! HEAVY-FOOTED CLUMMOXES.
HOW ABOUT HEAVY FOOT AN' CLUMMOX?
DASHER, SMASHER, DUNDER, BLITZEN AN' CLUMMOX ?
MIZ RABBIT SEEM TO BE GAININ'... SHE GOT A FAST PAIR OF FEET.
OL' BEAR RUNS LIKE A VERITABLE WATERMILLION!
YUM
POGO, THAT YUM IS JES' THE WORD I IS LOOKIN' FOR--- I'D LIKE TO IN-VITE YOU OVER TO YOUR PLACE FOR LUNCH.
GEE THANKS.
SOMEBODY THERE ALL READY! THE NERVE!
YO' IDEA SEEM TO OF BEEN POPULAR, CHURCHY.
WELL! WELL! WHAT A SURPRISE! WELCOME HOME, POGO!
QUICK, HIDE THE GOODIES, OWL--- IT'LL JES' CAUSE TALK.
POGO

THOOD FOR FOUGHT!

BY JING! GITTIN' RID OF MIZ RABBIT A-CHASIN' ME JES' CAUSE I ACCIDENTAL BROKE DOWN HER HOUSE WAS THE HIGH POINT OF MY CAREER ---- NOW -- WHAT HAPPENED TO THEM TWO NO GOOD REINDEERS?

IMAGINE THEM RUNNIN' OFF WHEN I WAS IN DIRE PERIL --- AFTER ALL I DID FOR 'EM --- GIVED 'EM GOOD JOBS ALL SUMMER AN' FALL. --- OH, IT DON'T PAY TO BE A SANDY CLAUS.

I'LL JEST GO OVER TO POGO'S HOUSE, SET DOWN AN' EAT HIS GRUB AN' WAIT FOR HIM TO COME BACK IF IT TAKES 47 YEARS.

OH, I'LL GIVE IT TO HIM -- 47 YEARS!

IT'S THAT ROOSIAN SANDY CLAUS! COME TO PUT POGO IN A SLAVE CAMP FOR FORTY-SEVEN YEARS!

ONLY ONE THING TO DO-- UNDER THE **POTATO SALAD**; QUICK.
HEY!
CLEVER WORK!
SO!
GREETINGS, COMMISSAR! POGO AIN'T HERE!
GOOD! I'LL EAT POTATO SALAD WHILE I WAITS.
WELL--UH--
I WON'T LET HIM PUT NO MUSTARD ON YOU.
I LIKE PURE POTATO SALAD WITHOUT NO POTATOES IN HER.
HOWEVER--
HOW DOES **YOU** ACCOUNT FOR THE **POTATO SALAD** SITTIN' AT THE **HEAD** OF THE **TABLE**?
JES' A MATTER OF TASTE-
PSSST-- OL' BEAR THINKS YOU IS **PURE** POTATO SALAD--- HE DON'T KNOW YOU IS PART POSSUM.

Panel 1:

"MAN AN' BOY, I IS BEEN A *POTATO SALAD* FANCIER AN' I *NEVER* SAW NONE SIT DOWN WITH FOLKS LIKE THAT."

"HOW *ELSE* WOULD IT SIT DOWN WITH FOLKS, 'CEPT *LIKE THAT*?"

"SURE, *POTATO SALAD DON'T* GOT LEGS AN' ARMS AN' BONES AN' BRAINS—"

"DON'T GO TOO FAR."

Panel 2:

"MIND IF I SET HERE AN' THINK ABOUT ALL THIS?"

"I'LL HELP YOU."

"IT'S *HARD* FOR POTATO SALAD TO SPEAK FOR ITSELF—SO WE PUT IT THERE WITHOUT *ASKIN'*."

Panel 3:

"DOES YOU MEAN *THIS* POTATO SALAD IS *LIKE PEOPLE*? IT GOT FEELIN'S?"

Panel 4:

"*PHOO!* IT LOOKS TO ME LIKE PERTY *DUMB ORDINARY* POTATO SALAD."

Panel 5:

WOWP

"*SEE!* NOW YOU IS BROKE ITS LI'L' POTATO SALAD HEART."

YOWP WOWP WHOOP OW
YOU KIN SEE HOW YOU IS INSULTED THE POTATO SALAD!
LISTEN AT IT WHIMPER--
WHEEP! WHOW!
NEVER HEARD TELL OF TALKIN' POTATO SALAD.
OH- LEMME CLIMB UP HERE AND TELL YOU--
DON'T THE PITEOUS CRIES OF THE POTATO SALAD AWAKE NO WHATSOEVER REMORSE IN YO' STONY BREAST?
OOOH- YO' THOUGHTLESS REMARKS IS TORED IT'S LI'L' HEART STRINGS TO PIECES.
YOWP YOWP
STOP BITIN' POGO'S TAIL BONE.
MA
PA
OH! WHOOP! YOWP! HOO HA! OOH-WOWP! OH-HOO! WHOO HEE!
S'POSE I IS INSULTED THE POTATO SALAD--- WHY'S THAT GIVE YOU THE LEAPIN' WILLIES?

'CAUSE I CLIMBED UP ON THAT HOT STOVE TO TELL YOU SO!
NOW THAT YOU IS ADMITTED YOU INSULTS THE POTATO SALAD, THE LEAST YOU KIN DO IS A-POLOGIZE!
I NEVER ADMITTED NOTHIN'! I JEST SAID S'POSE! S'POSE! S'POSE!
OOP! WOW! YHA-HO!
IN THAT CASE GO! AN' NEVER DARKEN OUR DOOR AGAIN!
HOW COME THEY THRUN YOU OUT, LITTLE MOTHER?
POGO
'CAUSE I WOULDN'T APOLOGIZE TO THE POTATO SALAD.
A CIVIL ANSWER WOULDN'T HURT NONE, LADY.
BEARS CAN'T BE BLAMED-- NOTICE HOW STUPID HER CHILD LOOKS?
LONG AS BOTH WAS THROWED OUT BY ALBERT, US IS IN THE SAME BOAT, OWL.
'PEARS LIKE IT.

SHARE AN' SHARE ALIKE.
R I G H T
THRU THICK AN' THIN!
RIGHT!
`TIL YOUR DEATH DO US PART!
MY DEATH? WHY ME?
`CAUSE YOU'LL STARVE FIRST, ALACK ADAY.
BUT LI'L' FELLAS DON'T NEED AS MUCH TO EAT AS BIG FELLAS.
YOU AIN'T GONNA GIT AS MUCH.
I WILL TOO! I'LL BREAK A PRECEDENT-- I'LL EAT HOME!
NORMALLY I WOULDN'T BE SO RASH---BUT SINCE THEM BOLSHEVINKS STOLT THE STATE OF GEORGIA I'D JEST AS SOON STEAL IT BACK BIT BY BIT--- EATIN' MY OWN GRUB WILL HELP.
OWL
GOSH--THIS ALL BEEN STOLT BY THE REEVOLUTIONARIES?
I'M FROM VIRGINIA-- YOU S'POSE THEM RASCALS STOLED VIRGINIA TOO?
COULD OF-- UNLESSEN THEY PASSED A ANTI-MACASSAR ACT WHICH THROWS THE WHOLE THING INTO THE LAP OF THE CHAIRMAN.

122

SOB SOB!
HUSH YOUR LOUD SOBBIN'--YOU IS ONLY ASSUMIN' THERE ISN'T NO VIRGINIA, YO' NATIVE STATE AN' HOME TOWN.
I BETS YOU THERE ISN'T NO VIRGINIA--THEM BOLSHEVINKS MUST IS STOLT THAT'N TOO.
PRIDE! PRIDE!
AS A OL' AN' HONORABOBBLE SANDY CLAWS I BETS YOU THAT BOLOGNA TO A MILLION DOLLARS I IS RIGHT!
SANDY, THAT'S A GOOD EVEN BET--WAIT THERE.
BEHIND OF THIS SCREEN HE'LL NEVER SEE ME WRITIN' OUT THIS LETTER WHAT IS SHEER PROOF!
HERE'S DOCUMENT'RY EVIDENCE--JES' IN FROM OL' JOHN COLBURN, IN RICHMOND. IT SAY: "DEAR SANTA CLAUS: YES, THERE IS A VIRGINIA." REPEAT: "DEAR SANTA CLAUS: YES, THERE IS A VIRGINIA!"
I GUESS THAT REDUCES THE WHOLE ARGUMENT TO A MIZERBLE ABSURDIDITTY.
THAT'S THE WAY I FELT FINALLY... SO WHILE YOU WAS FORGIN' THAT... I ATE THE BOLOGNA.

ALL SWELL

"DOGGONE, POGO, YOU IS ALLUS BUSY."

"WELL-- YOU KNOW, IT'S THAT TIME OF YEAR WHEN US TAKES TIME OFF FROM WORRYIN' 'BOUT OURSELFS AN' THINKS OF OTHERS."

"YEP-- AN' I IS DOIN' IT-- I BEEN THINKIN' OF PRESIDENT POLK ALL DAY--"

"PHOO-- YOU SPENT ALL NIGHT ADDRESSIN' CARDS."

"HO HUM! ADDRESSIN' ONE CARD, YOU MEANS-- AN' THEN IT WAS SPELT WRONG."

"PHOO! I SOLVED THE CARD PROBLEM-- I PUT TO X FROM X ON EVERY ONE OF 'EM-- IT'S LEGAL."

"HOW'D YOU SPELL THAT 'FROM'?"

"GOSH! WHAT ABOUT THE LI'L BEAR CHILLUN?"

"I'LL JES' TAKE MY PRESENTS AN' POGO'S SANDY SUIT AN' PLAY SANDY CLAWS TO 'EM-- THEIR PAP IS LEFT 'EM ALONE."

SUIT'S A LI'L' SNUG BUT A GOOD LOOKIN' MAN MAKE A GOOD APPEARANCE IN ANYTHING HE THROW ON.
MAN! DIN'T THINK I'D GIT HERE IN TIME.
ONLY THOUGHTFUL FOLKS LIKE ME IS THOUGHTFUL -- THIS IS A GREAT IDEA TO PLAY SANDY CLAWS TO THE BEAR TADS. I DESERVE CREDIT, GREAT CREDIT.
OL' BEAR
THIS IS MY TERRITORY, FRIEND! BACK OFF!
WHEN I DISPENSES BROTHERLY LOVE, FRIEND --
NO DOGGONE BEAR IS GONE STOP ME!
WELCOME TO OUR EASTER PARTY, YOU TWO OL' SANTY CLAUSES.
EASTER PARTY?!
US LAID A EGG, B'RER RABBIT.

A Few Backwords

IT IS NOT so easy these days to sound a simple, clearheaded note of hysteria, but my friend Bill Vaughan, crafty columnist of the Kansas City *Star* and the NANA Service, working hand in glove with a certain cartoonist, is positive that the bugle with which to blow such a blast has been found.

Drift-finders, an organization devoted to the wetting of the wind with a forefinger, has discovered that the ordinary man in the street only appears to be smarter than his leaders both at home and abroad. In the January 1958 report, *Just Plumb Bob,* Mr. Vaughan indicates that there is every reason to believe that heads of government, statesmen, and other people with yellow briefcases and blue suits, are just playing at being stupid.

"If we are in a race with Russia," says Vaughan, "we cannot merely pretend to be stupid; we will have to be genuine idiots. WE MUST OUTSTUPEFY THE RUSSIANS."

That seems to be the key phrase: OUTSTUPEFY THE RUSSIANS. There is not much time left. But we have the material, the men, the know-how and somewhat of a tradition in the field.

In a letter to Mr. Vaughan outlining his thoughts on the subject, a dirt farmer in Dirt, New Braska, said: "My dirt crop isn't what it used to be, but, then, it never was. Trouble is with these government people. Most of them are half-bred idiots. What we have got to get is pure-bred idiots. I don't go for these new crops of idiots that got nothing like the stupidity of like when we were younger. I have found that

I get smarter as I get older, a condition that has done me no good in the party of my heart.

"You'll hear a lot of people tell you, 'The older I get the more stupid I get' or 'Shucks, the older I get the more stupid I get.' Some do it with a 'Shucks' and some do it raw, but it amounts to the same thing—pigwash. It's my belief and the belief of my sister's husband, Perle (he's the one with the mole), that this assumption of expanding ignorance is a pose and not a very graceful one at that.

"It's all right to strike an attitude of genius; that is every man's prerogative, like being born in a log cabin or burying your kin if they are dead. Anybody can pretend to be smart and get away with it, because, who is to say? But it takes the McCoy to pass yourself off as an ass or an idiot.

"Right there is where true blue blood counts. The blue corpuscles of the average idiot run very deep, in my opinion, and, I might add, Perle agrees. Right now we have got red corpuscles in the government and white corpuscles too, but the blue corpuscle is not represented there in the quantity that we think."

So ends the dirt farmer's letter. Most of us will probably agree that it is a brave and clarion call to increased brainlessness. There is some doubt that we will be able to reach our peak or even a reasonable stride in 1958. But there is no reason to think that we cannot all be numbskulls by 1959.

It is probably not too soon to warn again that our leaders in business, education and government are merely pretending to be stupid. As Mr. Vaughan suggests, we might give everyone a close check from now on. Genuine idiocy should be our goal. Remember, we must outstupefy the Russians in '59. There may be no '60. Rise, Dolts, you have nothing to lose but your brains.